SOLE SELLING AGENT
ALEXANDER BROUDE, INC.
120 W. 57th STREET - NEW YORK, N.Y. 10019

The Treasury of

ENGLISH CHURCH MUSIC

ONE: 1100–1545
TWO: 1545–1650
THREE: 1650–1760
Volume FOUR: 1760–1900
FIVE: 1900–1965

General Editors: Gerald H. Knight and William L. Reed

The Treasury of
ENGLISH

BLANDFORD PRESS : LONDON

CHURCH MUSIC

Volume FOUR 1760–1900

Edited by GERALD H. KNIGHT
and WILLIAM L. REED
With an Introduction by GEORGE GUEST

FIRST PUBLISHED IN 1965

167 HIGH HOLBORN, LONDON, W.C.1

LIBRARY OF CONGRESS
CATALOGUE NUMBER 65-25006

TEXT FILMSET IN BASKERVILLE BY BOOKPRINT LIMITED.
MUSIC ENGRAVED BY N.V. GEBR. KEESMAAT, HAARLEM, HOLLAND.
PRINTED IN HOLLAND BY N.V. GEBR. KEESMAAT AND
BOUND IN GREAT BRITAIN BY RICHARD CLAY (CHAUCER PRESS)
LIMITED, BUNGAY, SUFFOLK.

GENERAL EDITORS' PREFACE

IT is perhaps not unreasonable to state that no other country possesses so fine and unbroken a choral tradition as England, and to claim that English Church music at its best compares with the finest to be found anywhere in the world.

Like the householder in the Gospel, the editors have sought to bring forth out of this 'treasure, things new and old', from the earliest experiments in polyphony to the challenging compositions of today, and in the compilation of the first three volumes they have been assisted by eminent musicians, each of whom is a specialist in his own field.

Volume 1, which covers the earliest period to the Reformation, is edited by Denis Stevens.

Volume 2, representing the 'golden age' from the Reformation until the death of Charles I, is edited by Peter le Huray.

Volume 3, containing works from the early days of the Commonwealth to the accession of George III, is edited by Christopher Dearnley.

Much of the material in the above volumes is published for the first time, and a number of well-known pieces appear in newly-edited versions.

Volume 4 covers the period from 1760 to 1900, and includes an introduction by George Guest.

Volume 5 contains the works of twentieth-century composers (British, Canadian, Australian, and American) and includes an introduction by David Lumsden.

It is hoped that this publication will stimulate all who have an interest in Church Music to explore further the treasures that exist. What is of even greater importance, it is hoped that choirs throughout the world will be encouraged to sing this music worthily to the glory of God, for their own inspiration and that of very many others who listen to it.

GERALD H. KNIGHT
WILLIAM L. REED

View of the ORCHESTRA and Performers in Westminster Abbey,
during the Commemoration of HANDEL.

The first Handel Festival in Westminster Abbey, 1784

CONTENTS

ACKNOWLEDGMENTS

THE editors wish to thank Dr. J. Dykes Bower and Mr. George Guest for their kindness in reading the proofs and Mr. Malcolm Walker for his assistance with the discography.

Acknowledgment is also due to those publishers who have given permission for the inclusion of copyright material as indicated at the foot of the music pages.

G.H.K.
W.L.R.

Samuel Sebastian Wesley
from Groves' Dictionary of Music (*Macmillan*)

INTRODUCTION

ONE often meets with the generalization that this period was the least fruitful of all as far as the composition and performance of cathedral music was concerned. In some ways, certainly for the first hundred years, this is probably true, although it has always been more fashionable to blame the musicians than it has been to blame those who bore responsibility by statute—the cathedral clergy. But provincial cathedral organists of the eighteenth and nineteenth centuries had little standing, either socially or in the cathedral hierarchy; the all-important body was the Chapter, consisting of a Dean and from three to six Canons. Here lay the final authority, but there rarely went with it any musical qualification for such a responsibility, and the musical offering of the choirs is known to have been abysmally bad in all but a very few establishments. There were a number of contributory causes, but they all spring from apathy, self-satisfaction and a lack of direction. Not only was the repertoire extremely limited, but there was seldom even a full complement of competent lay-clerks. Samuel Sebastian Wesley writes that 'attending Evensong at Christ Church, Oxford, I remarked to the Organist, Dr. Marshall, "Why, you have only one man in surplice today, and him I can't hear!" The reply was "No, he is only a beginner".' The effect of all this on a cathedral musician can be imagined. 'Painful and dangerous', Wesley continues, 'is the position of a young musician who, after acquiring great knowledge of his art in the Metropolis, joins a country cathedral. At first he can scarcely believe that the mass of error and inferiority in which he has to participate is habitual and irremediable. He thinks he will reform matters, gently, and without giving offence; but he soon discovers that it is his approbation and not his advice that is needed.' Ralph Banks was appointed Organist of Rochester Cathedral in 1790. On taking over his new position he wrote, 'When I came from Durham to this cathedral in 1790 only one lay-clerk attended during each week. The daily service was chanted. Two settings of the Canticles (Aldrich in G and Rogers in D), and seven anthems had been in rotation on Sundays for twelve years.' The choir in Hereford Cathedral on Easter Day 1833 consisted of boys and one man (the Dean's butler) who sang bass. Things were even worse in Wales. Bangor Cathedral had no choir at all in 1802 (though the stipend of the Bishop was £6000 a year), and it is recorded that the only musical instrument in Llandaff Cathedral in 1850 was a bass viol. Even in Westminster Abbey there were still no full rehearsals in 1875. In a real sense, too, the provincial cathedral organist was cut off from any professional contact with his colleagues. Small wonder, therefore, that his enthusiasm waned and, understandably, his standards deteriorated; and one is not surprised to find that almost everything of worth, either of composition or of performance, was centred in London, at least until the second half of the nineteenth century.

Just as the clergy can be fairly blamed for what happened in the first hundred or so years of the period under review, so they can be commended for their subsequent attempt to improve matters. The Oxford Movement was not concerned solely with doctrine; its supporters also campaigned for decency and order to be brought back to cathedral and church worship, and music was included in this long overdue spring-cleaning. We see, therefore, new and vigorous efforts being made by such organists as Sir John Stainer at St. Paul's Cathedral, but this time with the help and support of the Cathedral clergy. Gradually, towards the end of the nineteenth century, this movement spread to the provinces and, with improving standards, composers once again began to take cathedral choirs seriously. The music they produced came almost entirely under continental influences and was perhaps of mean stature when compared with the symphonic masterpieces emanating from other European countries, but it nevertheless was sincere. It was, at least, more up to date than much of the cathedral music being produced today.

It seems clear that another musical by-product of the Oxford Movement was a new interest in plainsong, especially in those churches where Tractarian principles were followed. This had some influence on the later nineteenth-century composers, especially Stanford, and parts of his Service in B flat are largely built on plainsong; so is his Evening Service on the second and third Tones. In the early part of the century there had been an example of the influence of plainsong in Samuel Wesley's fine motet *In exitu Israel*, but plainsong was clearly suspect and not until the second half of the century did it begin to be generally accepted. This tolerance and even approbation was to lead to a new edition of Merbecke's *Booke of Common Praier Noted*, which, though not in fact true plainsong, was near enough to it to provide a spur to Martin Shaw and others in the early twentieth century.

Our information about church music (as distinct from cathedral music) is necessarily scanty, but there is no doubt about the general way in which services were rendered. A large number of churches still had no organ and choirs were normally accompanied by an orchestra which would be recruited locally and which would be placed with the choir at the west end of the church in a gallery. We read that in Sheffield Parish Church, in about 1800, 'before the west window was an immense box hung in chains, into which, by the aid of a ladder, musicians and singers, male and female, contrived to scramble, and with the aid of bum basses, hautboys, fiddles and various other instruments, accompanying shrill and stentorian voices, they contrived to make as loud a noise as heart would wish.' The music performed was a selection of metrical psalms and perhaps a few simple anthems; undoubtedly the results were, in the main, cacophonous. The church orchestras were superseded by the barrel organ, and then, in the 1840's, there was introduced from France the harmonium (never, perhaps, has an instrument been more inappropriately named).

The influence of the Oxford Movement was almost wholly beneficial to church music. One of its first results was the gradual abolition of the west end musicians' gallery and the placing of the choir into seats in the chancel. It was at about this time, too, that the choir was put into surplices; and, as this revolution in parish choral worship proceeded, no parish was satisfied until its church possessed an organ. By the beginning of this century, most did. But many were poor instruments, cheap and shoddily constructed, and often ill-fitted for their purpose; for the idea of the organ as a musical instrument in its own right had been forgotten, and it had come to be regarded merely as an imitation of the orchestra. By the end of the nineteenth century most churches had done away with metrical psalm-singing in favour of the system in common use today—the singing of the Psalms, according to the Prayer Book, to Anglican chants. This system had been in use in cathedrals since the Restoration in 1660, but there had been no standardization until, in 1808, the then Organist of Norwich Cathedral wrote, 'Suppose the organist and choir were to meet every morning and evening for one month and agree in the proper place in each verse of the Psalms where the reciting should end in both the first and last parts of the chant, and place under that particular word or syllable a conspicuous red mark; if one book were thus marked the others might be rendered similar to it. The benefit would be that all the members of the choir might recite as one person, and all come together to that word which they are previously sure is the most proper to end the recital.' From this rather tentative beginning a move towards unanimity was made, although not until the last forty years or so has any attention generally been paid to the *meaning* of the words, and to their correct accentuation.

In all choral music, whether sacred or secular, there has through the centuries been a never-ending difference of opinion as to the relative importance of the words and the music. The Council of Trent (1543–1563) dealt with this particular problem, so did Pope Pius X in his Motu Proprio of 1903. The Church of England, on the other hand, has until recently tended to lack direction and advice on the subject. At all events, there is no doubt that at the time of Henry Purcell and his immediate predecessors and successors correct word-assentuation and mood-painting were an integral part of the composition of cathedral music. It was in the middle of the eighteenth century that this principle of enhancing the meaning of the words by the music began to be laid aside. The blame for this is sometimes, quite erroneously, laid at the door of Handel; but, if native composers were supposed to be so influenced by one who, after all, was writing in what was for him a foreign language, it is not unreasonable to suppose that they might also have imitated his strength of melody, harmony and, above all, form. The truth, surely, lies in the fact that secular influences on composers of limited talent resulted in church music which was fitting neither from a liturgical nor from a musical point of view. Throughout this barren period, however, the earlier Restoration tradition of correct accentuation was never entirely lost. One can trace it through the works of Battishill, the two Wesleys and Walmisley to Parry, Stanford and the other less important composers contemporary with them.

The most difficult acquisiton of all for a composer is a personal and individual style, and the composers of this period should not be unduly blamed because of the derivative nature of most of their compositions. It has been said that the musical life of any period is only partly a product of its age; there are those composers (Mozart and Beethoven were amongst them) who take over a musical legacy from the past and try to develop and enlarge it; there are those too (perhaps the best example is Brahms) who are largely content to write in the style of bygone masters, whilst there are others who attempt to make a clean break with the past (such as the early Florentine operatic composers or Schoenberg). Nevertheless it is odd that authorities, both clerical and musical, still largely resist works coming from representatives of this third group. Aesthetic nostalgia for the outmoded is no new phenomenon and we find that most composers in the period under review wrote either in the style of a bygone age or in a development (usually harmonic) of that style.

The cathedral music of most late eighteenth-century composers owes much stylistically to Handel and to the stage music of the time, the influence of the latter being especially marked in those sections calling for the use of solo voices. Samuel Wesley looked more to the music of J. S. Bach, and the strength and logic of his counterpoint make him one of the most important composers of cathedral music. Samuel Sebastian Wesley inherited his father's love of Bach, but also very clearly owes much of his harmonic style, with its experimental use of chromaticism, to Spohr. Attwood and Walmisley, on the other hand, came more under the influence of Mozart, especially in the movements they wrote for solo voices. It is interesting to note, in passing, how much more successful English composers were in their choruses than in their solo sections; this is a generalization which is largely true for the first hundred years of the period. Towards the end of the nineteenth century, in spite of the writings of George Bernard Shaw, the music of Brahms became very widely known and admired in England, and his characteristic harmonic and melodic style was imitated by the two English composers who are, above all, regarded as being responsible for the renaissance in English cathedral music—Parry and Stanford. So great was the influence of Brahms that even minor composers gave up writing in the harmonic and melodic style of Mendelssohn and Gounod, though formally they still owed much to them.

No two authorities will agree as to the desirability or otherwise of emotion in sacred music. Yet, in many ways, Christianity *is* an emotional concept and it seems valid to doubt the existence of an unemotional yet sincere Christian. Emotion, therefore, would not only seem to be desirable in church music, but to be essential. But there is always the danger that the genuine religious emotion inherent in, say, the *Missa Brevis* by Palestrina, or in such an anthem as *Remember not, Lord, our offences* by Purcell, will degenerate in the work of a bad composer to a sentimentality so mawkish as to hide or distort the real meaning of the text (an example, perhaps, is *God is a spirit*, by Sterndale Bennett). The opposite danger is that the setting will be so commonplace and unemotional in all its aspects as to be still-born, a mere musical exercise which has no identity with the text it seeks to illustrate. Much of the music in this period is open to one or other of these criticisms, and that is perhaps why, during no less than one hundred and forty years, so little of lasting worth was written.

Nevertheless, there were some works of genuine merit in this period, for no aesthetic period is wholly bad; but it has not proved easy for the layman to distinguish them from the less good. The pendulum of critical approval and disapproval has swung more extremely than usual and we are only now coming towards a historical and objective appraisal of a period of cathedral and church music which for many is too near their own time to view with dispassion.

GEORGE GUEST St. John's College, Cambridge

CALENDAR OF EVENTS

1760 Accession of George III.
Boyce's *Cathedral Music, Volume 1* published.

1765 Birth of Attwood.

1766 Birth of Samuel Wesley.

1768 Boyce's *Cathedral Music, Volume 2* published.

1775 Birth of Crotch.

1778 Boyce's *Cathedral Music, Volume 3* published.
New pedal organ added to the Westminster Abbey organ.
Death of Arne.

1779 Death of Boyce.

1781 *Sacred Harmony* published by John and Charles Wesley.

1784 Birth of Spohr.
First Handel Commemoration in Westminster Abbey.

1788 Death of Charles Wesley.

1790 Arnold's *Cathedral Music* published.

1791 Death of John Wesley

1793 Death of Benjamin Cooke.

1800 Birth of Goss.

1801 Death of Battishill.

1802 Death of Arnold.

1809 Birth of Mendelssohn.

1810 Birth of Samuel Sebastian Wesley.

1812 Crotch's *Palestine* produced.

1813 Birth of Henry Smart.
Samuel Wesley's edition of Bach's *48* published.
London Philharmonic Society founded.

1814 Birth of Walmisley.

1816 Birth of Sterndale Bennett.

1818	Birth of Gounod.
1820	Accession of George IV. Spohr's first visit to England.
1823	Foundation of the Royal Academy of Music.
1825	Birth of Ouseley.
1826	Birth of Steggall.
1829	Mendelssohn's first visit to England.
1830	Accession of William IV.
1832	Passing of the Reform Bill. Mendelssohn's second visit to England.
1833	Oxford Movement. John Keble's sermon on National Apostasy.
1837	Accession of Queen Victoria. Death of Samuel Wesley. Mendelssohn conducts *St. Paul* at the Birmingham Festival.
1838	Death of Attwood.
1839	Spohr's *Calvary* performed at the Norwich Festival.
1840	Birth of Stainer.
1841	*Sacred Hymns from the German* (Frances Cox) published.
1842	Birth of Sullivan.
1846	Mendelssohn's *Elijah* performed at the Birmingham Festival.
1847	Death of Mendelssohn. Death of Crotch. Rimbault's edition of Arnold's *Cathedral Music* published. Spohr's *The Last Judgment* and *The Fall of Babylon* performed in London.
1848	Birth of Parry.
1849	Bach Society founded by Sterndale Bennett. S. S. Wesley's *A Few Words on Cathedral Music* published.
1852	Birth of Stanford.
1854	Bach's *St. Matthew Passion* first performed in England.
1856	Death of Walmisley. St. Michael's College, Tenbury, founded.
1857	Birth of Elgar.
1859	Death of Spohr.
1860	Organs and surpliced choirs established in parish churches.
1861	*Hymns Ancient and Modern* published.
1863	*Chorale Book for England* (Catherine Winkworth) published.
1865	Royal College of Organists founded.

1866 Birth of Charles Wood.
Death of John Mason Neale.

1867 Sterndale Bennett's *The Woman of Samaria* produced.
Birth of T. Tertius Noble.

1869 Birth of Walford Davies.

1870 Gounod visits London and organizes the Gounod Choir.

1872 Birth of Vaughan Williams.

1874 Birth of Holst.
Birth of Bairstow.

1875 Death of Sterndale Bennett.
Trinity College of Music founded.

1876 Death of S. S. Wesley.
Death of J. B. Dykes.

1879 Death of Henry Smart.
Birth of John Ireland.

1880 Death of Goss.
Guildhall School of Music founded.
Birth of Edgar Bainton.
Birth of Healey Willan.

1882 Gounod's *La Rédemption* performed at the Birmingham Festival.

1883 Royal College of Music founded.

1885 Gounod's *Mors et vita* performed at the Birmingham Festival.

1887 Stainer's *The Crucifixion* performed.
Parry's *Blest Pair of Sirens* performed.

1889 Death of Ouseley.

1891 *Cathedral Prayer Book* (Haines) published.
Birth of Bliss.

1892 Parry's *Job* performed.
Birth of Howells.

1893 Death of Gounod.

1895 Birth of Sowerby.

1896 Elgar's *The Light of Life* performed.

1899 *Yattendon Hymnal* published.

1900 Elgar's *The Dream of Gerontius* performed at the Birmingham Festival.
Death of Sullivan.

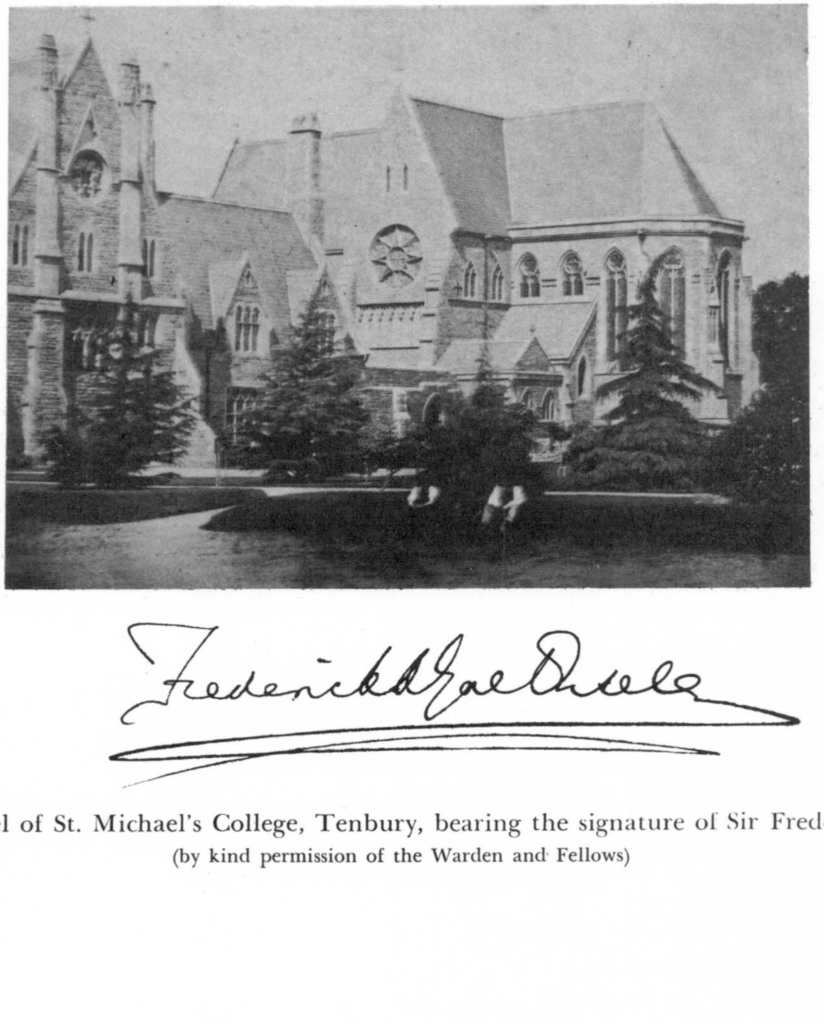

The Chapel of St. Michael's College, Tenbury, bearing the signature of Sir Frederick Ouseley
(by kind permission of the Warden and Fellows)

MAGNIFICAT

FROM THE EVENING SERVICE IN G

Edited by
W. L. REED

BENJAMIN COOKE (1734-1793)

10
He hath re - gard - ed the low - li - ness, the low - li - ness of
He hath re - gard - ed the low - li - ness, the low - li - ness of
He hath re - gard - ed the low - li - ness, the low - li - ness of
He hath re - gard - ed the low - li - ness, the low - li - ness of
CAN.
mf
15
His hand - maid - en. For be - hold, from hence - forth all ge - ne-
His hand - maid - en. For be - hold, from hence - forth all,
His hand - maid - en. For be - hold, from hence - forth all ge - ne-
His hand - maid - en. For be - hold, from hence - forth all,
20
-ra - tions, all ge - ne - ra - tions shall call me
all ge - ne - ra - tions, all ge - ne - ra - tions shall call me
-ra - tions, all ge - ne - ra - tions shall call me
all ge - ne - ra - tions shall call, shall call me

FULL 25
bless - ed, shall call me bless - ed. For He that is migh - ty hath
FULL
bless - ed, shall call me bless - ed. For He that is migh - ty hath
FULL
bless - ed, shall call me bless - ed. For He that is migh - ty hath
FULL
bless - ed, shall call me bless - ed. For He that is migh - ty hath
f Gt.
30 cresc.
mag - ni - fi - ed me, and ho - ly, ho - ly, ho - ly
cresc.
mag - ni - fi - ed me, and ho - ly, ho - ly, ho - ly
cresc.
mag - ni - fi - ed me, and ho - ly, ho - ly, ho - ly
cresc.
mag - ni - fi - ed me, and ho - ly, ho - ly, ho - ly
(Full Sw.) p
cresc.
DEC. 35
is His Name. And His mer - cy is on them that fear
DEC.
is His Name. And His mer - cy is on them that fear
DEC.
is His Name. And His mer - cy is on them that fear
DEC.
is His Name. And His mer - cy is on them that
(Ch.) mf

CAN.
40
mf
Him, through-out all ge-ne-ra-tions. He hath shew-ed
fear Him, through-out all ge-ne-ra-tions. He hath shew-ed
Sw. mf
strength, hath shew-ed strength with His arm;
FULL
He hath scat-ter-ed the
Gt.
45
f
He hath scat-ter-ed the proud in the i-ma-gi-
proud, He hath scat-ter-ed the proud in the i-ma-gi-
He hath scat-ter-ed the proud in the i-ma-gi-na-

50
mf DEC.
-na - tion of their hearts. He hath put
-na - tion of their hearts. He hath put
-ma - gi - na - tion of their hearts. He hath put down the
- tion of their hearts. He hath put down the
Sw.
55
FULL
down the migh - ty from their seat, and hath ex -
down the migh - ty from their seat, and hath ex -
migh - ty from their seat, from their seat, and hath ex - alt -
migh - ty from their seat, from their seat, and hath ex - alt -
Gt.
Gt. f
60
DEC.
-alt - ed, ex - alt - ed the hum - ble and meek. He hath fill - ed the
-alt - ed, ex - alt - ed the hum - ble and meek. He hath
-ed, ex - alt - ed the hum - ble and meek. He hath fill - ed the
-ed, ex - alt - ed the hum - ble and meek. He hath
mf
Ped.

65
hun - gry— with— good— things, and the rich He hath sent emp-ty a-
fill - ed the hun-gry with good things, and the rich He hath sent emp - ty a-
hun - gry with— good— things, and the rich hath sent,
fill - ed the hun-gry with good things, and the rich He hath sent
Ped.
70
CAN.
-way, He hath sent emp - ty a - way. He re-
-way, He hath sent emp - ty a - way. He re-
He hath sent emp - ty, sent emp - ty a - way. He re-
emp - ty a - way, He hath sent emp - ty a - way. He re-
75
-mem - b'ring His mer - cy hath hol - pen His ser - vant— Is - ra-
-mem - b'ring His mer - cy hath hol - pen His ser - vant— Is - ra-
-mem - b'ring His mer - cy— hath— hol - pen His ser - vant— Is - ra-
-mem - b'ring His mer - cy hath hol - pen His ser - vant— Is - ra-

80
-el; As He pro-mis-ed to our fore-fa-thers, A-bra-
-el; As He pro-mi-sed to our fore-fa-thers, A-bra-
-el; As He pro-mis-ed to our fore-fa-thers, A-bra-
-el; As He pro-mis-ed to our fore-fa-thers, A-bra-
85
-ham, A-bra-ham and his seed, for ev-er.
-ham, A-bra-ham and his seed, for ev-er.
-ham, A-bra-ham and his seed, for ev-er.
-ham, A-bra-ham and his seed, for ev-er.
FULL
90
Glo-ry, glo-ry be to the Fa-ther, and to the Son, and to the Ho-ly
FULL
Glo-ry, glo-ry be to the Fa-ther, and to the Son, and to the Ho-ly
FULL
Glo-ry, glo-ry be to the Fa-ther, and to the Son, and to the Ho-ly
FULL
Glo-ry, glo-ry be to the Fa-ther, and to the Son, and to the Ho-ly
Gt. f

95
Ghost; As it was in the be - gin - ning, is now, and ev - er shall
Ghost; As it was in the be - gin - ning, is now, and ev - er shall
Ghost; As it was in the be - gin - ning, is now, and ev - er shall
Ghost; As it was in the be - gin - ning, is now, and ev - er shall
100
ff
be, world with - out end. A - - - - - - - - - - - - -
be, world with - out end. A - - - - - - - - - - - -
be, world with - out end. A - - - - - - - - - - - -
be, world with - out end. A - - - -
rall.
105
men.
men.
men.
men, A - - - - - - - - - - - men.

O LORD, LOOK DOWN FROM HEAVEN

Edited by
GEORGE C. MARTIN

JONATHAN BATTISHILL (1738-1801)

mf 15
from heav'n, O Lord, look down from heav'n,
heav'n, O Lord, look down from heav'n, look down from heav'n, look down from
Lord, look down, look down from heav'n, O Lord, look
mf
O Lord, look
20 dim.
25 mf
look down from heav'n, and be-hold,
dim. mf
heav'n, look down from heav'n, and be-hold, be-
dim. mf
down, look down from heav'n, and be-hold, be-hold,
dim. mf 1st. BASS
down, look down from heav'n, and be-
dim. mf

30
be - hold ___ from the ha - bi - ta - tion of Thy ho - li-ness and
- hold, ___ be - hold from ___ the ha - bi - ta - tion of Thy ho - li-ness
from the ha - bi - ta - tion of Thy ho - li-ness
be - hold,
2nd. BASS
- hold, and be - hold, be - hold from the ha - bi - ta - tion of Thy ho - li-ness
cresc.
ff
35
of Thy glo - ry:
cresc.
ff
f>
and of Thy glo - ry: where ___ is Thy zeal, Thy zeal ___
cresc.
ff
f>
and of Thy glo - ry: where ___ is Thy zeal, Thy zeal ___ and Thy
cresc.
ff
f
and of Thy glo - ry, and ___ of Thy glo - - -
cresc.
ff
f

1ST SOPRANO
2ND SOPRANO
40
f
and Thy strength, Thy zeal and Thy
f
where is Thy zeal, Thy zeal, where is Thy zeal, Thy zeal
and Thy strength, where, where, O Lord,
strength, and Thy strength, where is Thy zeal, Thy zeal, Thy zeal and Thy
-ry,
45
strength, where is Thy zeal,
and Thy strength, Thy strength, Thy zeal and Thy strength, where, O where is Thy
where is Thy zeal and Thy strength, where
strength, where is Thy zeal, Thy zeal and Thy strength, where is Thy
f
where is Thy zeal, Thy zeal and Thy strength, where

50
55
where is Thy strength, where is Thy zeal and Thy
zeal, Thy zeal and Thy strength, where is Thy zeal, where
is Thy zeal and Thy strength, where is Thy zeal and Thy strength, Thy strength
zeal, Thy zeal and Thy strength, where is Thy zeal, Thy zeal and Thy
is Thy zeal and Thy strength, where is Thy zeal, Thy zeal and Thy
60
cresc.
strength, Thy zeal and Thy strength, where is Thy
is Thy zeal and Thy strength, where is Thy
Thy zeal and Thy strength, where is Thy zeal, where is Thy
strength, Thy zeal and Thy strength, where is Thy zeal, Thy zeal and Thy
1ST. BASS
strength, and Thy strength, and Thy strength, Thy zeal, is Thy
2ND. BASS
strength, and Thy strength, where is Thy zeal, is Thy

65
zeal, Thy zeal and Thy strength, where is Thy zeal and Thy
zeal, Thy zeal and Thy strength, and Thy strength, where is Thy zeal and Thy
strength, Thy zeal and Thy strength, where is Thy zeal and Thy
strength, Thy zeal and Thy strength, Thy zeal and Thy strength, where is Thy zeal and Thy
1st. & 2nd. BASS.
zeal, and Thy strength, where is Thy zeal and Thy
70
ff
strength, Thy zeal and Thy strength, where is Thy zeal and Thy
strength, Thy zeal and Thy strength, where is Thy zeal and Thy
strength, Thy zeal and Thy strength, where is Thy zeal and Thy
strength, Thy zeal and Thy strength, where is Thy zeal and Thy
strength, Thy zeal and Thy strength, where is Thy zeal and Thy

strength,– Thy mer - cies to - wards me, Thy mer - cies
strength,– Thy mer - cies to - wards me, Thy mer - cies
strength, Thy mer - cies to - wards me, Thy mer - cies
strength,– Thy mer - cies to - wards me, Thy mer - cies
strength,– Thy mer - cies to - wards me, Thy mer - cies
to - wards me? are they– re - strain'd, are they–
to - wards me? are they– re - strain'd, are
1ST. ALTO
to - wards me? are– they re - strain'd, are they
2ND. ALTO
to - wards me? are they
to - wards me? are they re-strain'd, are they re -
to - wards me? are they re - strain'd, are they

90
95
mf cresc.
re - strain'd, are
they re - strain'd, are
re - strain'd, are
cresc.
re - strain'd, are they re - strain'd, are
1ST. TENOR
cresc.
-strain'd, are they re - strain'd, re - strain'd, are
2ND. TENOR
-strain'd, are they re - strain'd, re - strain'd,
re - strain'd, are they re - strain'd, are they re -
100
105
f
they re - strain'd, are they re - strain'd, re -
they re - strain'd, are they re - strain'd, re -
they re - strain'd, are they re - strain'd,
they re - strain'd, are they re - strain'd,
they re - strain'd, re - strain'd,
are they, are they re - strain'd,
-strain'd, re - strain'd, are they re - strain'd, are

dim.
p
110
rall.
dim.
115
- strain'd, are they re - strain'd?
- strain'd, are they re - strain'd?
are they re - strain'd, are they re - strain'd?
are they re - strain'd, are they re - strain'd, re - strain'd?
are they re - strain'd, are they re - strain'd?
are they re - strain'd, are they re - strain'd, re - strain'd?
they re - strain'd, are they re - strain'd?

NUNC DIMITIS

FROM THE EVENING SERVICE IN A

Edited by
W. L. REED

SAMUEL ARNOLD (1740-1802)

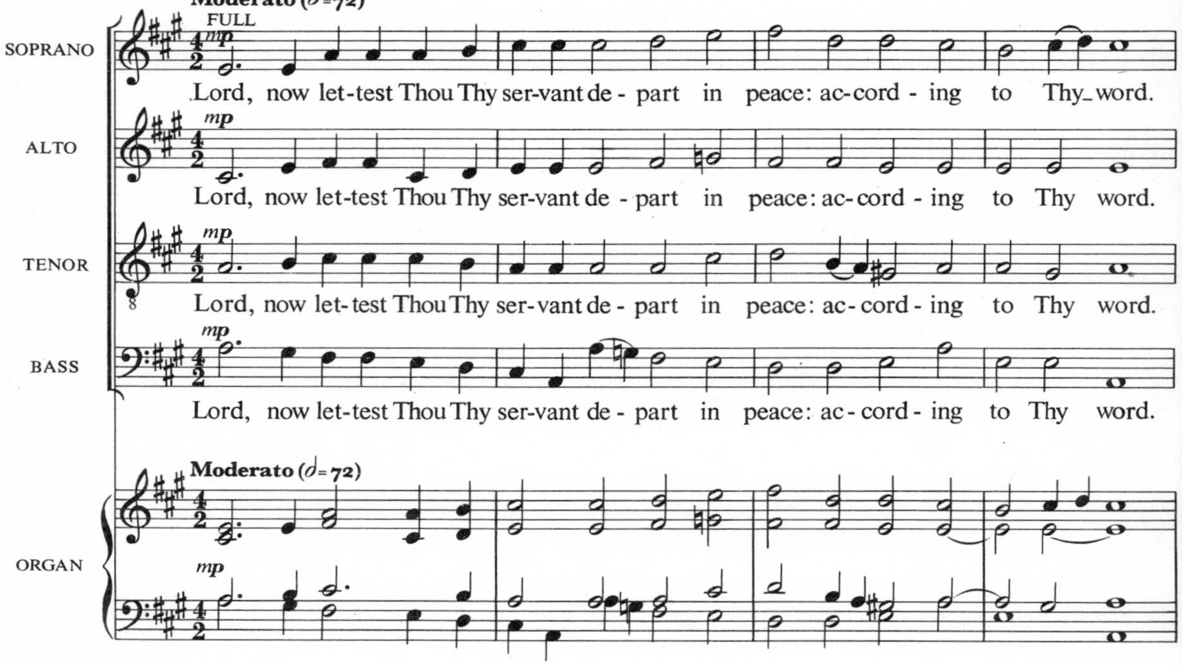

*originally 'the salvation'

VERSE
Meno mosso (𝅗𝅥 = 66)
To be a light to light - en the Gen - tiles: and to be the
glo - ry of Thy peo - ple Is - ra - el, to be the glo - ry of Thy
peo - ple Is - ra - el.
(𝅗𝅥 = 72) FULL
Glo - ry be to the Fa - ther,

25
and to the Son: and to the Ho - ly Ghost; As it
and to the Son: and to the Ho - ly Ghost; As it
and to the Son: and to the Ho - ly Ghost; As it
and to the Son: and to the Ho - ly Ghost; As it
30
was in the be - gin - ning, is now, and ev - er shall be: world with - out
was in the be - gin - ning, is now, and ev - er shall be: world with - out
was in the be - gin - ning, is now, and ev - er shall be: world with - out
was in the be - gin - ning, is now, and ev - er shall be: world with - out
35
end, A - - - - men, A - - men.
end, A - - - - - - - - - - - men.
end, A - men, A - - - men.
end, A - - men, A - - - men, A - - men.

COME, HOLY GHOST
(VENI CREATOR SPIRITUS)

Translated by
JOHN COSIN (1594-1672)

THOMAS ATTWOOD (1765-1838)

Larghetto
dolce
SOPRANO SOLO
ORGAN
cresc.
p
Ped.
f
Diaps.
p Sw.
1. Come, Ho - ly Ghost, our souls in - spire, And light - en with ce - les - tial fire;
Thou the a - noint - ing Spi - rit art,
Who dost Thy sev - en - fold gifts im - part:
Thy bless - ed unc - tion from a - bove Is com - fort, life, and fire of love, is com - fort, life, and fire of love.

(VOICES ALONE)
SOPRANO
ALTO
TENOR
BASS
For practice only
dolce
cresc.
p
35
40
45
2. Enable with perpetual light The dulness of our blinded sight: Anoint and cheer our soiled face With the abundance of Thy grace:

50
55
p
cresc.
Keep far our foes, give peace at home; Where Thou art Guide no
60
f
ill can come, where Thou art Guide no ill can come.
65
dolce
3. Teach us to know the Fa - ther,
f Diaps.
p Sw.

70
cresc.
p
Son, And Thee,– of Both, to be— but– One; That through the
Son, And Thee,– of Both, to be— but One; That through the
Son, And Thee, of Both, to be but One; That through the
Son, And Thee,– of Both, to be— but One; That through the
75
80
a - ges all— a - long This— may be— our end - less song,
a - ges all a - long This— may be— our end - less song,
a - ges all— a - long This— may be— our end - less song,
a - ges all— a - long This— may be— our end - less song,

85
Praise to Thy eternal mer-it, Fa-ther, Son, and
Praise to Thy e-ter-nal mer-it, Fa-ther, Son, and
Praise to Thy e-ter-nal mer-it, Fa-ther, Son, and
Praise to Thy e-ter-nal mer-it, Fa-ther, Son, and
90
Ho-ly Spi-rit, Fa-ther, Son, and Ho-ly Spi-rit.
Ho-ly Spi-rit, Fa-ther, Son, and Ho-ly Spi-rit.
Ho-ly Spi-rit, Fa-ther, Son, and Ho-ly Spi-rit.
Ho-ly Spi-rit, Fa-ther, Son, and Ho-ly Spi-rit.
95
mf Sw.
cresc.
100
dim.
p dim.
pp

TURN THY FACE FROM MY SINS

THOMAS ATTWOOD (1765-1838)

40
45
clean heart, O God, and re-new a right spi-rit with-in me, re-new, re-new, re-
clean heart, O God, and re-new a right spi-rit with-in me, re-new, re-
clean heart, O God, and re-new a right spi-rit with-in me, re-new, re-
clean heart, O God, and re-new a right spi-rit with-in me, re-new, re-new, re-
50
55
-new, re-new a right spi-rit with-in me, re-new a right spi-rit with-in me.
-new, re-new a right spi-rit with-in me, re-new a right spi-rit with-in me.
-new, re-new a right spi-rit with-in me, re-new a right spi-rit with-in me.
-new a right spi-rit, a right spi-rit with-in me, re-new a right spi-rit with-in me.
SOLO
60
65
Cast me not a-way, a-way from Thy pre-sence, and take not Thy Ho-ly Spi-rit

70
75
from me, and take not Thy Ho - ly Spi - rit _ from me, Thy Ho - ly Spi - rit _ from _ me.
CHORUS
80
85
S.
Cast me not a - way, ___ a - way _ from Thy pre - sence, and take not Thy Ho - ly
A.
Cast me not a - way, ___ a - way from Thy pre - sence, and take not Thy Ho - ly _
T.
Cast me not a - way, ___ a - way _ from Thy pre - sence, and take not Thy Ho - ly
B.
Cast me not a - way, ___ a - way _ from Thy pre - sence, and take not Thy Ho - ly
90
95
Spi - rit _ from me, and take not Thy Ho - ly Spi - rit _ from me, Thy Ho - ly Spi - rit _ from _ me.
Spi - rit from me, and take not Thy Ho - ly Spi - rit from me, Thy Ho - ly Spi - rit from _ me.
Spi - rit from me, and take not Thy Ho - ly Spi - rit from me, Thy Ho - ly _ Spi - rit from _ me.
Spi - rit from me, Thy Ho - ly Spi - rit from me.
(senza Ped.)
Ped.

SING ALOUD WITH GLADNESS
(EXULTATE DEO)

SAMUEL WESLEY (1766-1837)

15
God of Ja - - - - - - - cob, Sing a -
De - o Ja - - - - - - - cob, Ex - ul -
sing, and praise the God of Ja - cob, Sing a -
ju - bi - la - te De - - - o Ja - cob, Ex - ul -
un - to God our Help - - er, sing, and praise the God of
ad - ju - to - ri nos - - tro, ju - bi - la - te De - o,
f
Sing, and praise the God of
Ju - bi - la - te De - o,
20
25
- loud with glad - ness un - to God our Help - - er,
- ta - te De - o ad - ju - to - ri nos - - tro,
- loud with glad - ness un - to God our Help - - er, sing, and
- ta - te De - o ad - ju - to - ri nos - - tro, Ju - bi -
Ja - cob, praise the God of Ja - - - - cob, sing, and
Ju - bi - la - te De - - o Ja - - - - cob, Ju - bi -
Ja - cob, praise the God of Ja - - cob,
Ju - bi - la - te De - - - o Ja - - cob,
Sing a - loud with
Ex - ul - ta - te

30
sing, and praise the God of Ja - cob, sing, and praise the
ju - bi - la - te De - o Ja - cob, ju - bi - la - te
praise the God of Ja - cob, sing, and praise the
-la - te De - o Ja - cob, ju - bi - la - te
praise the God of Ja - cob, sing, and praise the
-la - te De - o Ja - cob, ju - bi - la - te
sing, and praise the God of Ja - cob,
Ju - bi - la - te De - o Ja - cob,
glad - ness un - to God our Help - er, sing, and praise the
De - o ad - ju - to - ri nos - tro, ju - bi - la - te
35
God of Ja - cob, sing a - loud with glad -
De - o Ja - cob, ex - ul - ta - te De -
God of Ja - cob, sing a - loud with glad -
De - o Ja - cob, ex - ul - ta - te De -
God of Ja - cob, sing a - loud with glad -
De - o Ja - cob, ex - ul - ta - te De -
sing a - loud with glad - ness un - to God our Help -
ex - ul - ta - te De - o ad - ju - to - ri nos -
God of Ja -
De - o Ja -

40
45
-ness, sing, and praise the God of Ja-cob, sing, and praise the God of
-o, ju-bi-la-te De-o Ja-cob, ju-bi-la-te De-o
-ness, sing, and praise the God of Ja-cob, sing, and praise the God of
-o, ju-bi-la-te De-o Ja-cob, ju-bi-la-te De-o
-ness, sing, and praise the God of Ja-cob, sing, and praise the God of
-o, ju-bi-la-te De-o Ja-cob, ju-bi-la-te De-o
-ness, sing, and praise the God of Ja-cob, sing, and praise the God of
-o, ju-bi-la-te De-o Ja-cob, ju-bi-la-te De-o
-cob, sing a-loud with glad-ness, sing a-loud, and praise the God of
-cob, ju-bi-la-te De-o, ju-bi-la-te De-o, De-o
50
Ja - cob, sing a-loud with glad-ness, sing a-
Ja - cob, ju-bi-la-te De-o, ex-ul-
Ja - cob, sing, and praise the God of Ja-
Ja - cob, ju-bi-la-te De-o Ja-
Ja - cob, sing a-loud with glad-ness, sing with
Ja - cob, ju-bi-la-te De-o, ju-bi-
Ja - cob, sing with glad-ness, sing with glad-ness,
Ja - cob, ju-bi-la-te, ju-bi-la-te,
Ja - cob, sing, and praise the God of Ja-
Ja - cob, ju-bi-la-te De-o Ja-

55
- loud with glad - ness un - to God our Help - - - -
- ta - te De - o ad - ju - to - - - ri nos - - - - -
- - - cob, sing a - loud with glad - ness un - to God our Help - -
- - - cob, ex - ul - ta - te De - o ad - ju - to - ri nos - -
glad - ness, sing a - loud with glad - ness un - to God our Help - -
- la - te, ex - ul - ta - te De - o ad - ju - to - ri nos - -
sing, and praise the God of Ja - - - - - - - -
ju - bi - la - te De - o Ja - - - - - - - -
- - - cob, sing a - loud with glad - ness un - to God our Help - -
- - - cob, ex - ul - ta - te De - o ad - ju - to - ri nos - -
60
- er, sing, and praise the God of Ja - cob,
- tro, ju - bi - la - te De - o Ja - cob,
f
- er, sing a - loud with glad - ness, sing a - loud with glad - ness,
- tro, ju - bi - la - te De - o, ex - ul - ta - te De - o
- er, sing, and praise the God of Ja - - cob, sing, and praise the
- tro, ju - bi - la - te De - o Ja - - cob, ju - bi - la - te
- cob, sing, and praise the God of Ja - cob,
- cob, ju - - bi - - la - - te De - o Ja - cob,
- er, sing, and praise the God of Ja - - - - - - - - cob,
- tro, ju - bi - la - te De - o Ja - - - - - - - - cob

65
70
sing, and praise the God of
ju - bi - la - te De - o
unto God our Help - - er, sing, and praise the God of
ad - ju - to - ri - nos - - tro, ju - bi - la - te De - o
God of Ja - - - - - - - cob, sing a - loud with
De - o Ja - - - - - - - cob, ju - bi - la - te
God of Ja - - - cob, sing with
De - - - o Ja - - - cob, ex - ul -
sing, and praise the God of Ja - cob, sing, and praise the
ju - bi - la - te De - o Ja - cob, ju - bi - la - te
75
Ja - - cob,
nos - - tro,
Ja - - cob,
nos - - tro,
glad - - ness, sing, and praise the God of Ja - - - - -
De - - o, ju - bi - la - te De - - o Ja - - - -
glad - ness, sing a - loud with glad - ness unto God our Help - -
- ta - te, ex - ul - ta - te De - o ad - ju - to - ri nos -
God of Ja - - - - - - - - - - - - - -
De - o Ja - - - - - - - - - - - - - -
f

80
sing a - loud with glad - ness un - to God our Help - - er,
ex - ul - ta - te De - o ad - ju - to - ri nos - - tro,
sing a - loud with glad - ness un - to God our Help - - - - - -
ex - ul - ta - te De - o ad - ju - to - ri nos - - - - - -
- cob, sing a - loud with glad - ness un - to God our Help - er, un -
- cob, ex - ul - ta - te De - o ad - ju - to - ri nos - tro, ad -
- er, sing with glad - ness un - to God our Help - er. Come ye with mu - sic,
- tro, ex - ul - ta - te De - o ad - ju - to - ri. Su - mi - te psal - mum,
- cob, sing with glad - ness un - to God our Help - er. Come ye with mu - sic,
- cob, ex - ul - ta - te De - o ad - ju - to - ri. Su - mi - te psal - mum,
85
90
Come ye with mu - sic, strike ye the ta - bou-ret,
Su - mi - te psal - mum, et da - te tym - pa-num,
- er, God our Help - er. Come ye, and strike ye the ta - bou-ret,
- tro, ad - ju - to - ri. Su - mi - te et da - te tym - pa-num,
- - - to God our Help - er. Come ye with mu - sic, come ye with
- - - ju - to - ri nos - tro. Su - mi - te psal - mum, su - mi - te
come ye with mu - sic, come ye with
su - mi - te psal - mum, su - mi - te
strike ye the ta - bou-ret, strike ye, strike ye, strike ye the ta - bou-ret,
et da - te tym - pa-num, da - te, da - te, et da - te tym - pa-num,

95
mu - sic, sing a - loud with glad - - ness un - to
psal - mum, ex - ul - ta - te De - - o ad - ju -
mu - sic, strike ye the ta - bou-ret, strike the ta - bou-ret. and
psal - mum, et da - te tym - pa-num, da - te tym - pa-num, ju -
sing a - loud with glad - - ness un - to God our
ex - - ul - ta - te De - - o ad - ju - to - ri
100
come ye with mu - sic, strike ye the ta - - -
su - mi - te psal - mum, et da - te tym - - -
come ye with mu - sic, strike ye the ta - - -
su - mi - te psal - mum, et da - te tym - - -
God our Help - - - - er, un - to God our
- to - ri nos - - - - tro, ad - ju - to - - - ri
bring ye the pleas - ant harp and psal - te - ry,
- cun - dum psal - te - ri - um cum ci - tha-ra,
Help - - - er, come ye with mu - sic, strike ye the ta - bou-ret,
nos - - - tro, su - mi - te psal - mum, et da - te tym - pa-num,

105
- - - bou-ret, Sing a - loud with glad - - - ness un - - - to
- - - pa-num, Ex - ul - ta - te De - - - o ad - - - ju - - -
- - - bou-ret, Sing a - loud with glad - - - ness un - - - to
- - - pa-num, Ex - ul - ta - te De - - - o ad - - - ju - - -
Help - er, Sing, and praise the God of Ja - - -
nos - tro, Ju - bi - la - te De - o Ja - - -
Come ye with mu - sic, and strike the ta - bou-ret,
Su - mi - te psal - mum, et da - te tym - pa-num,
Sing a - loud with glad - ness un - to God our Help - - -
Ex - ul - ta - te De - o ad - ju - to - ri nos - - -
110
God, to God our Help - er, Come ye with
- to - - - ri nos - tro De - o, Su - mi - te
God, to God our Help - er, strike ye the ta - bou-ret,
- to - - - ri nos - tro De - o, et da - te tym - pa-num,
- - - - - - cob, Come ye with mu - sic, come ye,
- - - - - - cob, Su - mi - te psal - mum, su - mi - te,
Come ye with mu - sic and
Su - mi - te psal - mum, Ju -
- er, Come ye with mu - sic, strike ye the ta - bou-ret,
- tro, Su - mi - te psal - mum, et da - te tym - pan-um,

115
120
mu - sic, strike ye the ta - bou-ret,
psal - mum, et da - te tym - pa-num,
come ye, strike ye the ta - bou-ret,
psal - mum, et da - te tym - pa-num,
Sing with glad-ness, sing, and praise the
Ju - bi - la - te, ex - ul - ta - te
p
bring ye the plea - sant harp, Sing a - loud with glad - ness unto-
- cun - dum psal - te - ri - um, Ex - ul - ta - te De - o ad - ju -
and bring ye the plea - sant harp, Come ye, come ye,
Ju - cun - dum psal - te - ri - um, da - te, da - te
p
125
p
Sing a -
Ex - ul -
p
Sing a -
Ex - ul -
p
God of Ja - cob, Sing a -
De - o Ja - cob, Ex - ul -
p
God our Help - er, Sing a -
to - ri - nos - tro, Ex - ul -
f
and bring ye the plea - sant harp, yea, come ye with mu - sic,
Ju - cun - dum psal - te - ri - um, et su - mi - te psal - mum
p

130
-loud with glad - ness un - to God our Help - er, Come ye with
-ta - te De - o ad - ju - to - ri nos - tro, Su - mi - te
-loud with glad - ness un - to God our Help - - - er,
-ta - te De - o ad - ju - to - ri nos - - - tro,
-loud with glad - ness un - to God our Help - - - - - er,
-ta - te De - o ad - ju - to - ri nos - - - - - tro,
-loud with glad - ness, and bring ye the plea - sant harp, strike the
-ta - te tym - pa-num, ju - cun - dum psal - te - ri - um, da - te
strike ye the ta - bou-ret, and bring ye the plea - sant harp,
et da - te tym - pa-num, ju - - - cun - - dum psal - te - ri - um,
135
mu - sic, strike ye the ta - bou-ret, strike the ta - bou-ret,
psal - mum, et da - te tym - pa-num, da - te tym - pa-num,
sing a - loud with glad - ness un - to God our
Ju - bi - la - te De - o ad - ju - to - - - - ri
ta - bou-ret, sing with glad-ness, come ye with
tym - pa-num ad - ju - to - ri, su - mi - te
sing a - loud with glad - ness un - to God our Help - er,
ex - ul - ta - te De - o ad - ju - to - ri nos - tro,

140
f
sing a - loud with glad - ness unto God our
ex - ul - ta - te De - o ad - ju - to - ri
come ye with mu - sic, strike ye the ta - bou-ret, un - to God our
su - mi - te psal - mum, et da - te tym - pa-num ad - ju - to - ri
Help - er, un - to God our Help - er,
nos - tro, ad - ju - to - ri nos - tro,
mu - - - - sic un - to God our Help - er,
psal - - - - mum ad - ju - to - ri nos - tro,
come ye with mu - sic, strike ye the ta - bou-ret,
su - mi - te psal - mum, et da - te tym - pa-num,
145
150
p
Help - - er, sing a -
nos - - tro, ex - ul -
Help - - er, sing a -
nos - - tro, ex - ul -
sing a - loud with glad - ness un - to God our Help - - er, sing a -
ex - ul - ta - te De - o ad - ju - to - ri nos - - tro, ex - ul -
sing a - loud with glad - ness unto God our Help - - er, sing a -
ex - ul - ta - te De - o ad - ju - to - ri nos - - tro, ex - ul -
Sing, and praise the God of Ja - - - - - - - - cob, sing a -
Ju - bi - la - te De - o Ja - - - - - - - - cob, ex - ul -

155
-loud with glad - ness un - to God our Help - - er.
-ta - te De - o ad - ju - to - ri nos - - tro.
-loud with glad - ness un - to God our Help - - er.
-ta - te De - o ad - ju to - ri nos - - tro.
-loud with glad - ness un - to God our Help - er. Come ye with
-ta - te De - o ad - ju - to - ri nos - tro. Su - mi - te
-loud with glad - ness un - to God our Help - - er.
-ta - te De - o ad - ju - to - ri nos - - tro,
-loud with glad - ness un - to God our Help - er. Come ye with
-ta - te De - o ad - ju - to - ri nos - tro, Su - mi - te
160
Come ye with mu - sic, come ye, and strike ye the
Su - mi - te psal - mum, et da - te, et da - te
Come ye with mu - sic, and strike ye, strike ye,
Su - mi - te psal - mum, et da - te, da - te ju -
mu - sic, strike ye the ta - bou - ret, strike the
psal - mum, et da - te tym - pa - num, da - te
Come ye, and strike ye, strike ye the
Su - mi - te et da - te, et da - te
mu - sic, strike ye the ta - bou - ret, come ye with mu - sic, strike ye the
psal - mum, et da - te tym - pa - num, su - mi - te psal - mum, et da - te

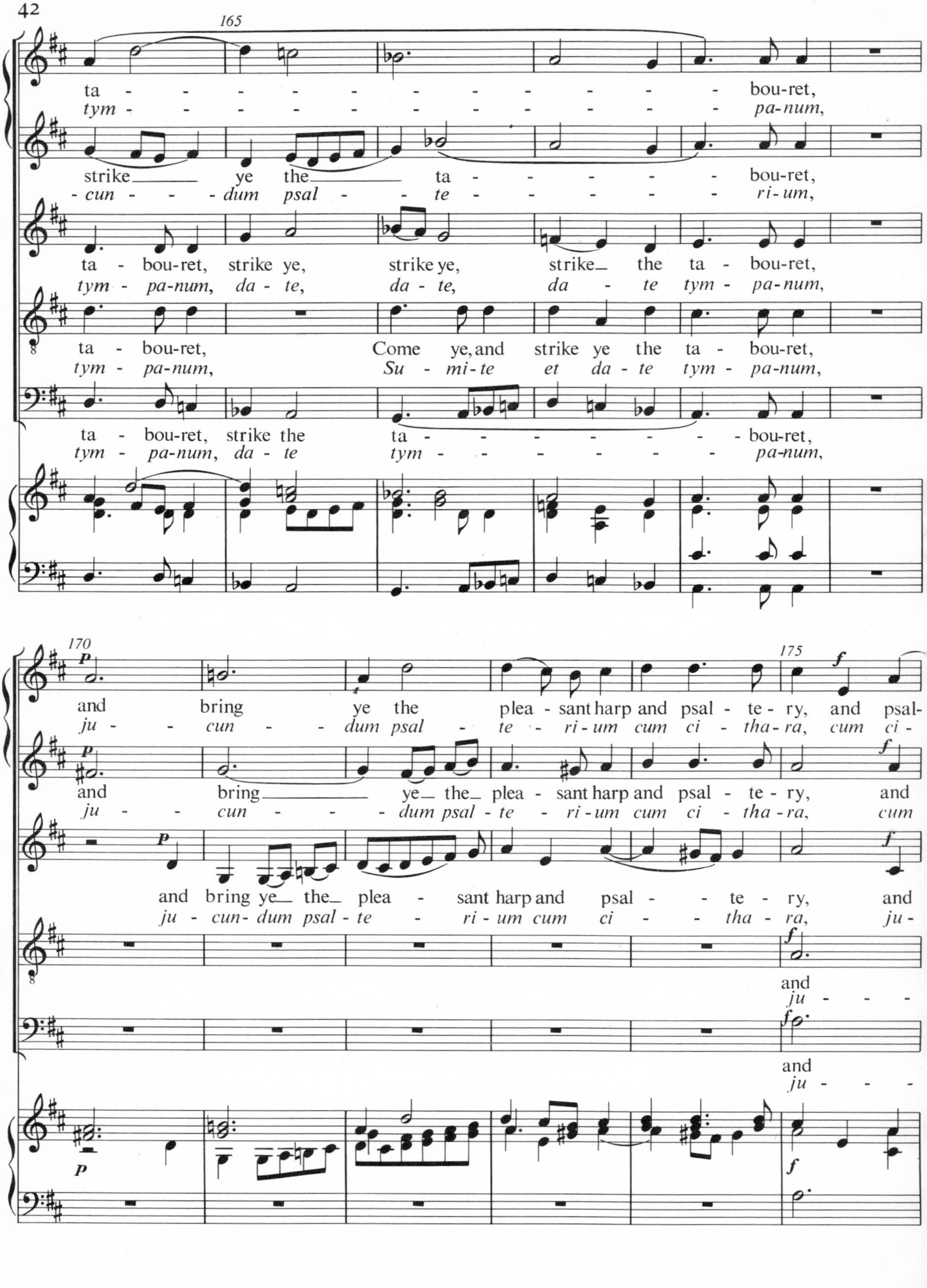
165
ta - - - - - - - - - - - - bou-ret,
tym - - - - - - - - - - - - pa-num,
strike ye the ta - - - - - - bou-ret,
-cun - - - dum psal - te - - - - - - ri-um,
ta - bou-ret, strike ye, strike ye, strike the ta - bou-ret,
tym - pa-num, da - te, da - te, da - te tym - pa-num,
ta - bou-ret, Come ye, and strike ye the ta - bou-ret,
tym - pa-num, Su - mi-te et da - te tym - pa-num,
ta - bou-ret, strike the ta - - - - - - - - bou-ret,
tym - pa-num, da - te tym - - - - - - - - pa-num,
170
175
and bring ye the plea - sant harp and psal - te - ry, and psal-
ju - cun - dum psal - te - ri-um cum ci - tha-ra, cum ci-
and bring ye the plea - sant harp and psal - te - ry, and
ju - cun - dum psal - te - ri-um cum ci - tha-ra, cum
and bring ye the plea - sant harp and psal - te - ry, and
ju - cun- dum psal - te - ri - um cum ci - tha - ra, ju-
and
ju - - -
and
ju - - -

180
te - ry, Sing a -
tha - ra, Ex - ul -
psal - te - ry, Sing a -
tha - ra, Ex - ul -
bring ye the plea - sant harp and psal - te - ry, Sing a -
-cu - dum psal - te - ri - um cum ci - tha - ra, Ex - ul -
bring ye the plea - sant harp and psal - te - ry, Sing a -
-cun - dum psal - te - ri - um cum ci - tha - ra, Ex - ul -
bring ye the plea - sant harp and psal - te - ry, Sing a -
-cun - dum psal - te - ri - um cum ci - tha - ra, Ex - ul -
185
-loud with glad - ness un - to God our Help - er, sing, and praise the
-ta - te De - o ad - ju - to - ri nos - tro, ju - bi - la - te
-loud with glad - ness un - to God our Help - er, sing, and praise the
-ta - te De - o ad - ju - to - ri nos - tro, ju - bi - la - te
-loud with glad - ness un - to God our Help - er, sing a - loud with
-ta - te De - o ad - ju - to - ri nos - tro, ju - bi - la - te
-loud with glad - ness un - to God our Help - er, sing, and praise the
-ta - te De - o ad - ju - to - ri nos - tro, ju - bi - la - te
-loud with glad - ness un - to God our Help - er, sing, and praise the
-ta - te De - o ad - ju - to - ri nos - tro, ju - bi - la - te

190
195
God of Ja - - cob, sing, and praise the God of Ja - - - - -
De - o Ja - - cob, ju - bi - la - te De - o Ja - - - - -
God of Ja - - cob, sing, and praise the God of Ja - - - - -
De - o Ja - - cob, ju - bi - la - te De - o Ja - - - - -
glad - ness, sing a - loud with glad - ness un - to God our Help - - -
De - o, ex - ul - ta - te De - o ad - ju - to - ri nos - - -
God of Ja - - cob, sing, and praise the God of Ja - - - - -
De - o Ja - - cob, ju - bi - la - te De - o Ja - - - - -
God of Ja - - cob, sing, and praise the God of Ja - - -
De - o Ja - - cob, ju - bi - la - te De - o Ja - - -
200
f
p
- cob, sing a - loud with glad - ness un - to
- cob, ex - ul - ta - te De - o ad - ju -
- cob, sing, and praise the God of Ja - cob, sing with glad - ness un - to
- cob, ju - bi - la - te De - o Ja - cob, De - o, De - o ad - ju -
- er, sing, and praise the God of Ja - cob, sing with glad - ness un - to
- tro, ju - bi - la - te De - o Ja - cob, De - o, De - o ad - ju -
- cob, sing, and praise the God of Ja - cob, sing with glad - ness un - to
- cob, ju - bi - la - te De - o Ja - cob, De - o, De - o ad - ju -
- cob, sing a - loud with glad - ness un - to
- cob, ex - ul - ta - te De - o ad - ju -

205
God our Help - - er, sing, and praise the God of Ja - cob,
- to - ri nos - - tro, ju - bi - la - te De - o Ja - cob,
God our Help - - er, sing, and praise the God of Ja - cob,
- to - ri nos - - tro, ju - bi - la - te De - o Ja - cob,
God our Help - - er, sing, and praise the God of Ja - cob,
- to - ri nos - - tro, ju - bi - la - te De - o Ja - cob,
God our Help - er, sing, and praise the God of Ja - cob,
- to - ri nos - - tro, ju - bi - la - te De - o Ja - cob,
God our Help - - er, sing, and praise the God of Ja - cob,
- to - ri nos - - tro, ju - bi - la - te De - o Ja - cob,
210
215
ff
Come ye with mu - sic, strike ye the
Su - mi - te psal - mum et da - te
Come ye with mu - sic, strike ye the
Su - mi - te psal - mum et da - te
Come ye with mu - sic, strike ye the
Su - mi - te psal - mum et da - te
Come ye with mu - sic, strike ye the
Su - mi - te psal - mum et da - te
Come ye with mu - sic, strike ye the ta - bou-ret, strike the
Su - mi - te psal - mum et da - te tym - pa - num, da - te

220
ta - bou-ret, and bring ye the plea - - - sant harp and psal - te -
tym - pa-num, Ju - cun-dum psal - te - - - - ri - um cum ci - tha-
ta - bou-ret, and bring ye the plea - sant harp and psal - te -
tym - pa-num, Ju - - cun - dum psal - te - ri - um cum ci - tha -
ta - bou-ret, and bring ye the plea - sant harp and psal - - te -
tym - pa-num, Ju - cun - dum psal - te - ri - um cum ci - - tha -
ta - bou-ret,
tym - pa-num,
ta - bou-ret,
tym - pa-num,
p
225
- ry, and psal - te -
- ra, cum ci - tha -
- ry, and psal - te -
- ra, cum ci - tha-
- ry, and bring the plea - sant harp and psal - te -
- ra, ju - cun-dum psal - te - ri - um cum ci - tha-
and bring ye the plea - sant harp and psal - te -
ju - cun - dum psal - te - ri - um cum ci - tha-
and bring ye the plea - sant harp and psal - te -
ju - cun - dum psal - te - ri - um cum ci - tha-
f

230
235
-ry, Sing a - loud with glad - ness un - to God our Help - er,
-ra, Ex - ul - ta - te De - o ad - ju - to - ri nos - tro,
-ry, Sing a - loud with glad - ness un - to God our Help - er,
-ra, Ex - ul - ta - te De - o ad - ju - to - ri nos - tro,
-ry, Sing a - loud with glad - ness un - to God our Help - er, sing with
-ra, Ex - ul - ta - te De - o ad - ju - to - ri nos - tro, ju - bi -
-ry, Sing a - loud with glad - ness un - to God our Help - er, sing and
-ra, Ex - ul - ta - te De - o ad - ju - to - ri nos - tro, ju - bi -
-ry, Sing a - loud with glad - ness un - to God our Help - er, sing with
-ra, Ex - ul - ta - te De - o ad - ju - to - ri nos - tro, ju - bi -
240
sing with glad - ness, sing a - loud
ju - bi - la - te, ju - bi - la
sing with glad - ness, sing a - loud
ju - bi - la - te, ju - bi - la
glad - ness, sing with glad - ness, sing a - loud
-la - te, ju - bi - la - te, ju - bi - la -
praise the God of Ja - cob,
-la - te De - o Ja - cob,
glad - ness, sing with glad - ness, sing with
-la - te, ju - bi - la - te, ju - bi -

245
with glad - - ness, praise the God
- - te De - - o, De - - o, De - -
with glad - - ness, praise the God
- - te De - - o, De - - o, De - -
with glad - - ness, praise God, sing with
- - te De - - o, De - - o, ju - bi -
f
praise Him, sing with glad - - ness, sing with glad - - ness,
De - - o, ju - bi - la - - te, ju - bi - la - - te,
glad - - ness,
-la - - te,
250
of Ja - - - - - cob, Come ye with mu - sic,
-o Ja - - - - - cob, Su - mi - te psal - mum,
of Ja - - - - - cob, Come ye with mu - sic,
-o Ja - - - - - cob, Su - mi - te psal - mum,
glad - - ness, sing with glad - ness,
-la - - te De - o Ja - cob,
sing with glad - - ness,
Ju - bi - la - - te,
Come ye with mu - - sic, strike ye the
Su - mi - te psal - mum et da - te

255
sing with glad - ness un - to God our Help - er,
ex - ul - ta - te De - o ad - ju - to - ri,
sing with glad - ness un - to God our Help - er,
ex - ul - ta - te De - o ad - ju - to - ri,
Come ye, come ye with mu sic, come ye, come ye with mu sic,
Su - mi - te, su - mi - te psal - mum, su - mi - te, su - mi - te psal - mum
Come ye, come ye with mu - sic, strike ye the ta - bou-ret, sing a -
Su - mi - te, su - mi - te psal - mum, et da - te tym - pan-um, ex - ul -
ta - bou-ret, strike the ta - bou-ret, sing a -
tym - pan-um, da - te tym - pan-um, ex - ul -
260
265
sing a - loud with glad -
ex - ul - ta - te De -
sing with glad-ness, sing with glad -
ex - ul - ta - te De - o, De -
strike ye the ta - bou-ret, sing a - loud with glad -
et da - te tym - pan-um, ex - ul - ta - te De -
- loud with glad-ness, sing with glad - ness
- ta - te De - o, ex - ul - ta - te
ff
- loud with glad-ness, come ye, come ye with mu - sic, come ye with
- ta - te De - o, su - mi-te, su - mi - te psal - mum, su - mi - te

270
- ness, strike ye the ta - bou-ret, strike the
- o, et da - te tym - pa-num, da - te
- ness, strike ye the ta - - - bou-ret, strike the
- o, et da - te tym - - - pa-num, da - te
- ness, sing with glad - ness, strike ye, strike ye the ta - bou-ret, strike
- o, ex - ul - ta - te et da - te, et da - te tym - pa-num, da - - - -
un - to God our Help - er, strike the ta - bou-ret, strike the
De - o ad - ju - to - ri, da - te tym - pa-num, da - te
mu - sic, strike ye the ta - - - - - - - bou-ret, strike the
psal - mum, et da - te tym - - - - - - - pa-num, da - te
275
ta - bou-ret, strike the ta - bou-ret, and bring ye the
tym - pa-num, da - te tym - pa-num, ju - cun - dum psal-
ta - bou-ret, strike the ta - bou-ret, and bring ye the
tym - pa-num, da - te tym - pa-num, ju - cun - dum psal-
the ta - bou-ret, and bring ye the
- - - - - - te tym - pa-num, ju - cun - dum psal-
ta - bou-ret, strike the ta - bou-ret, and bring ye the
tym - pa-num, da te tym - pa-num, ju - cun - dum psal-
ta - bou-ret, strike the ta - bou-ret, and bring ye the
tym - pa-num, da - te tym - pa-num, ju - cun - dum psal-

280
285
plea - - sant harp and psal - - te - ry.
-te - - ri - um cum ci - - tha - ra.
plea - - sant harp and psal - - te - ry.
-te - - ri - um cum ci - - tha - ra.
plea - - sant harp and psal - - te - ry.
-te - - ri - um cum ci - - tha - ra.
plea - - sant harp and psal - - te - ry.
-te - - ri - um cum ci - - tha - ra.
plea - - sant harp and psal - - te - ry.
-te - - ri - um cum ci - - tha - ra.
290
295

LO! STAR-LED CHIEFS

FROM THE ORATORIO 'PALESTINE'

Words by
REGINALD HEBER (1783-1826)

WILLIAM CROTCH (1775-1847)

SOPRANO
ALTO
TENOR
BASS
15
p
Lo! star-led chiefs As - sy-rian o - dours bring, And
Lo! star - led chiefs As - sy- rian o-dours bring, And
Lo! star-led chiefs As - sy - rian o - dours bring,
Lo! star-led chiefs, lo! star-led chiefs As - sy - rian o - dours
dim.
bend - - ing Ma - gi, and bend - ing Ma - gi
bend - - ing Ma - gi seek their in - fant King, and bend - ing Ma - gi
bend - - ing Ma - gi, and bend - ing Ma - gi
bring, And bend-ing Ma - gi, bend - - ing Ma - gi, bend - ing Ma - gi

seek their in - fant King! Lo! star-led chiefs As - sy - rian o - dours
seek their in - fant King! Lo! star-led chiefs As - sy - rian o - dours bring, And
seek their in - fant King! Lo! star-led chiefs As - sy - rian o - dours bring, And
seek their in - fant King! Lo! star-led chiefs As - sy - rian o - dours
bring, And bend - ing Ma - gi, bend - ing Ma - gi, bend - ing Ma - gi seek their
bend - - ing Ma - gi,
bend - - ing Ma - gi, bend - ing Ma - gi, and bend-ing Ma - gi seek their
bring, bend - ing Ma - gi, and bend-ing Ma-gi seek their

in - fant King! bend - ing Ma - gi seek their in - fant King!
bend - ing Ma - gi, bend - ing Ma - gi seek their in - fant King!
in - fant King! seek their in - fant King!
in - fant King! bend - ing Ma - gi seek their in - fant King!
30
Mark'd ye,
Mark'd ye,

p
mark'd — ye, where, hov'r - ing o'er His head,
p
Mark'd ye, where, hov'r - ing, hov'r - ing o'er His
p
mark'd — ye, where, hov'r - ing, hov'r - ing o'er His
p
Mark'd ye, where, hov'r - ing o'er His head,
35
hov'r - ing o'er His head, o'er His ra - diant head, The
head, hov'r - ing o'er His head, o'er His ra - diant
head, hov'r - ing o'er His head, o'er His ra - diant
hov'r - ing o'er His head, hov'r - ing o'er His ra - - - diant

cresc.
f
dove's white wings ce - les - tial, ce - les - tial glo - ry shed,
head, The dove's white wings ce - les - tial glo - ry shed,
head, The dove's white wings ce - les - tial glo - ry shed,
head, The dove's white wings ce - les - tial glo - ry shed,
legato
(Ped.)
40
dim.
p
ce - les - tial glo - ry shed, ce - les - tial glo - ry
ce - les - tial glo - ry shed, ce - les - tial glo - ry
ce - les - tial glo - ry shed, ce - les - tial glo - ry
ce - les - tial glo - ry shed, ce - les - tial glo - ry

shed? Lo! star-led chiefs As-sy-rian o-dours bring,
shed? As-sy-rian o-dours bring, As-sy-rian o-dours
shed? As-sy-rian o-dours bring,
shed? Lo! star-led chiefs As-sy-rian o-dours bring,
45
And bend-ing Ma-gi seek their in-fant King!
bring, And bend-ing Ma-gi seek their in-fant King!
And bend-ing Ma-gi seek their in-fant, in-fant King, seek their in-fant
And bend-ing Ma-gi, and bend-ing Ma-gi,

50
Mark'd ye, mark'd ye, where, hov'-ring o'er His head, where,
Mark'd ye, where, hov'-ring o'er His ra-diant
King! Mark'd ye, mark'd ye, where, hov'-ring o'er His ra-diant
Mark'd ye, mark'd ye, where, hov'-ring o'er His head,
cresc.
hov'-ring o'er His head, o'er His ra-diant head, The dove's white wings ce -
head, o'er His ra-diant head, o'er His ra-diant head, The dove's white
head, o'er His ra-diant head, o'er His ra-diant head, The dove's white
o'er His ra-diant head, o'er His ra-diant head, The dove's white

55
f
-les - tial, ce - les - tial glo - ry shed? o'er His
wings ce - les - tial glo - ry shed? o'er His
wings ce - les - tial glo - ry shed? o'er His
wings ce - les - tial glo - ry shed? o'er His
(Ped.)
dim.
ra - diant head, Mark'd ye, where, hov'r - ing o'er His ra - diant head, The
ra - diant head, Mark'd ye, where, hov'r - ing o'er His ra-diant head,
ra - diant head, Mark'd ye, where, hov'r - ing, The
ra - diant head, The
dim.

60
dove's white wings ce - les - tial glo - ry shed, The dove's white wings ce - les - tial
The dove's white wings ce - les - tial glo - ry shed, The dove's white wings ce - les - tial
dove's white wings ce - les - tial glo - ry shed, The dove's white wings ce - les - tial
dove's white wings ce - les - tial glo - ry shed, The dove's white wings ce - les - tial
65
glo - ry shed?
glo - ry shed?
glo - ry shed?
glo - ry shed?
dim.
tr
p

IF WE BELIEVE THAT JESUS DIED

JOHN GOSS (1800 - 1880)

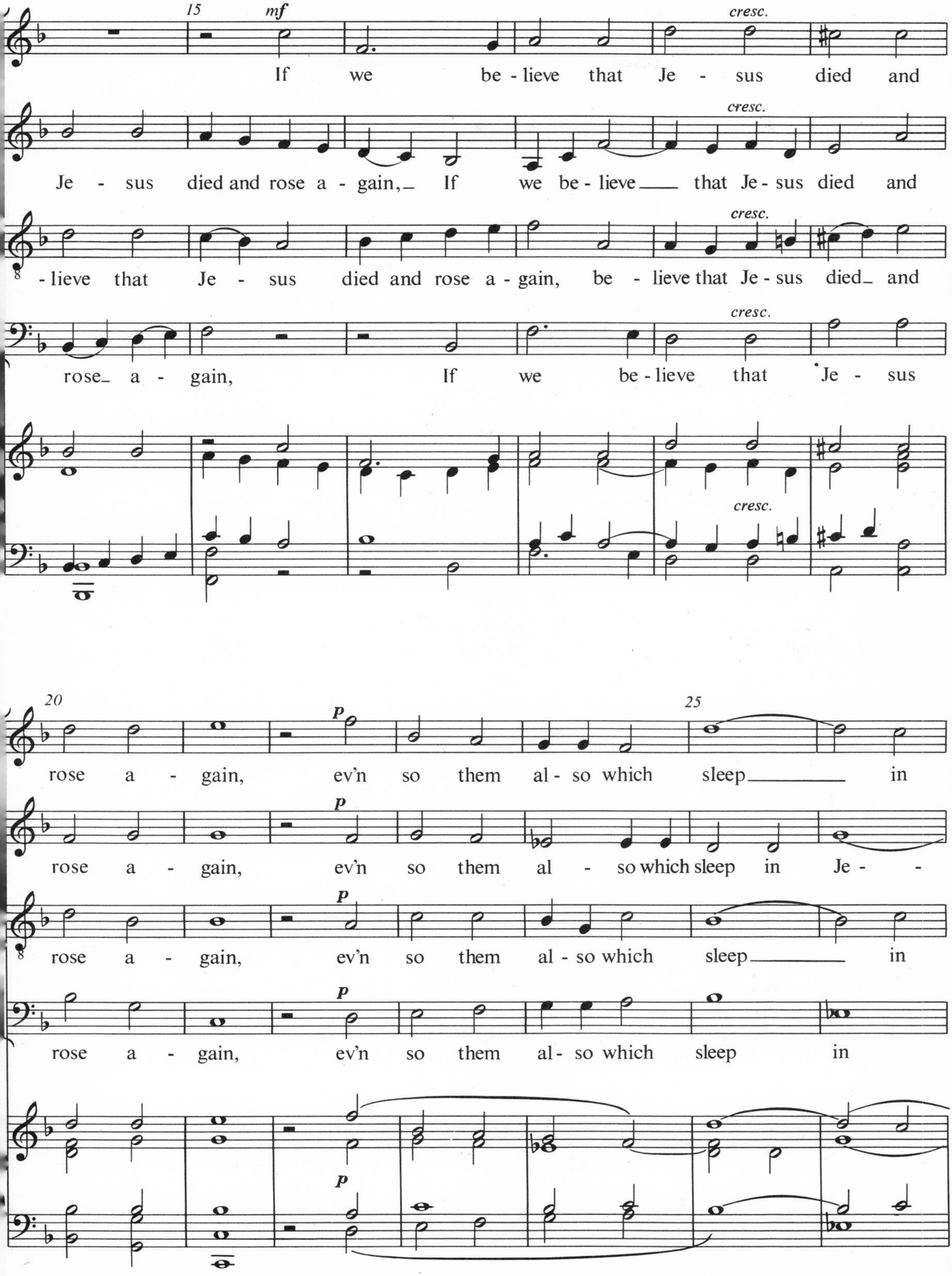
15
mf
cresc.
If we be - lieve that Je - sus died and
Je - sus died and rose a - gain, If we be - lieve that Je - sus died and
- lieve that Je - sus died and rose a - gain, be - lieve that Je - sus died and
rose a - gain, If we be - lieve that Je - sus
20
25
p
rose a - gain, ev'n so them al - so which sleep in
rose a - gain, ev'n so them al - so which sleep in Je -
rose a - gain, ev'n so them al - so which sleep in
rose a - gain, ev'n so them al - so which sleep in

30
cresc.
Je - sus, which sleep in Je - - sus, will God bring with Him, will
- sus, which sleep in Je - sus, will God bring with
Je - sus, which sleep in Je - - - sus,
Je - sus, sleep in Je - sus, will God
35
40
1ST SOPRANO
2ND SOPRANO
God will God bring with Him, will
God bring, will God bring with Him, will
Him, will God bring with Him,
will God, will God bring, will God
bring with Him, will God bring with Him, will

Unis.
45
mf
God bring with Him. If we be - lieve that Je - sus
will God bring with Him. If we be - lieve, if
bring with Him. If we be-
God bring with Him. If we be - lieve that
50
died, if we be - lieve that Je - sus died, that Je - sus
we be - lieve that Je - sus died, that Je - sus
- lieve that Je - sus died, that Je - sus died, and
Je - sus died, if we be - lieve that Je - sus died, if we be-

55
60
p
died and rose, and rose a - gain, ev'n
died and rose a - gain, ev'n
rose, and rose a - gain, ev'n
- lieve that Je - sus rose a - gain, ev'n
65
so them al - so which sleep in Je - sus, which sleep in
so them al - so which sleep in Je - - - sus, which sleep in
so them al - so which sleep in Je - sus, which sleep in
so them al - so which sleep in Je - sus, sleep in

70
cresc.
75
f
Je - - sus, will God bring with Him, will God,
Je - - sus, will God bring with Him, will
Je - - - - - - - sus, will God bring with
Je - - sus, will God,
80
will God bring with Him, will
God bring with Him, will
Him, will God bring with Him, will God
will God bring with Him, will God

85
God bring with Him, will God bring with
God bring with Him, will God bring with
bring, will God bring with
bring with Him, will God bring with
Slow (𝅗𝅥 = 56)
p
90
Him. Where-fore com - fort one a - no - ther with these words.
Him. Where-fore com - fort one a - no - ther with these words.
Him. Where-fore com - fort one a - no - ther with these words.
Him. Where-fore com - fort one a - no - ther with these words.
Slow (𝅗𝅥 = 56)
p

O SAVIOUR OF THE WORLD

JOHN GOSS (1800-1880)

10
help us, save us, and help us, O Sa- viour of the
Save us, and help us, save us, and help us, O Sa - viour of the
Save us, and help us, save us, and help us, O
Save us, and help us, save us, and help us, help
cresc.
15
world, O Sa - viour of the world, O Sa - viour, Who by Thy
world, O Sa - viour of the world, O Sa - viour, Who by Thy
Sa - viour of the world, of the world, O Sa - viour, Who by Thy
us, O Sa - viour of the world, O Sa - viour, Who by Thy
mf
cresc.
20
Cross and pre - cious Blood hast re - deem - ed us, Save us, and
Cross and pre - cious Blood hast re - deem - ed us, Save us, and
Cross and pre - cious Blood hast re - deem - ed us, Save us, and
Cross and pre - cious Blood hast re - deem - ed us,
f
dim.
p

help us, we hum-bly be-seech Thee, O Lord, we hum-bly be-seech Thee, O
help us, we hum-bly be-seech Thee, O Lord, we hum-bly be-seech Thee, O
help us, we hum-bly be-seech Thee, O Lord, we hum-bly be-seech Thee, be-seech Thee, O
help us, we hum-bly be-seech Thee, O Lord, we hum-bly be-seech Thee, O
Lord, O Sa - viour of the world, O
Lord, O Sa - viour of the world, O
Lord, O Sa - viour of the
Lord, O Sa - viour of the world, O save us, and
Sa - viour of the world, O Sa - viour, Who by Thy Cross and pre - cious
Sa - viour of the world, O Sa - viour, Who by Thy Cross and pre - cious
world, O Sa - viour of the world, Who by Thy Cross and pre - cious
help us, O Sa - viour, Who by Thy Cross and pre - cious
cresc.
sf

40
Blood hast re - deem - - ed us, Save us, and help us, we
Blood hast re - deem - - ed us, Save us, and help us, we
Blood hast re - deem - - ed us, Save us, and help us, we
Blood hast re - deem - - ed us, Save us, and help us, we
hum - bly be - seech Thee, O Lord, O Sa - viour of the world, Save us, and
hum - bly be - seech Thee, O Lord, O save us, Save us, and
hum - bly be - seech Thee, O Lord, O save us, Save us, and
hum - bly be - seech Thee, O Lord, O save us, Save us, and
45
Rather slower
help us, we hum - bly be - seech Thee, O Lord. A - men.
help us, we hum - bly be - seech Thee, O Lord. A - men, A - men.
help us, we hum - bly be - seech Thee, O Lord. A - men, A - men.
help us, we hum - bly be - seech Thee, O Lord. A - men.
Rather slower
cresc.
dim.
Ped.

BLESSED BE THE GOD AND FATHER

SAMUEL SEBASTIAN WESLEY (1810-1876)

15
cresc.
20
live - ly hope by the re - sur-rec-tion of Je - sus Christ from the dead,
live - ly hope by the re - sur-rec-tion of Je - sus Christ from the dead,
live - ly hope by the re - sur-rec-tion of Je - sus Christ from the dead,
live - ly hope by the re - sur-rec-tion of Je - sus Christ from the dead,
f Gt. Diaps., Sw. coupled
ALTO, TENOR AND BASS (Unison)
L'istesso tempo
25
To an in-her-it-ance in-cor-rup-ti-ble and un - de - fi - led, that
Gt. Open Diap., Sw. uncoupled
Ped.
30
fa - deth not a - way, re - serv - ed in heaven for you, Who are kept by the
35
pow - er of God, through faith un-to sal-va - tion rea-dy to be re-veal-ed in the

DEC. SOPRANO SOLO
last time. But as He Which hath
Sw. Reed.
Sw. Diaps.
Man.
call - ed you is ho - ly, so be_ ye ho - ly in all manner of_ con - ver -
- sa - tion. Pass the time of your so - journ-ing here in fear,_ in_ fear._
Allegretto (♩=104)
Love one an - o-ther with a
Clarabella
Sw. Princ.
rit.
Sw. Reed.
Ped.
CAN. SOPRANOS
pure_ heart fer - vent-ly, See that ye love_ one an - o - ther,

SOLO DEC.
75
CAN. SOPRANOS
Love one an - other with a pure_ heart_ fer - vent-ly, See that ye
80
SOLO DEC.
love one an - o - ther, Love one an - o-ther with a pure
85
heart fer - vent-ly, a pure heart fer - vent-ly,
CAN. SOPRANOS
90
SOLO DEC.
See that ye love one an - o - ther, See that ye love,_ that ye
95
love_ one an - o - ther with a pure heart fer - vent-ly.

100
DEC. SOPRANOS
CAN. SOPRANOS
with a
See that ye love one an - o - - ther with a
105
pure heart, a pure heart fer - vent-ly.
pure heart, a pure heart fer - vent-ly.
ALTO, TENOR AND BASS (Unison)
RECIT. ad lib.
Be-ing born a-gain, not of cor-rup-ti-ble seed, but of in - cor-rup - ti-ble, by the word of
Gt. Open Diap.
Ped.
110
God. For all flesh is as grass, and all the glo - ry of man as the flow - er of grass. The
Sw. Reed.
115
grass withereth, and the flow-er there-of fall - - eth a - way:
Clarabella
Sw. Reed.
f Full Org.

Allegretto (𝅗𝅥=100)
ff
But the word of the Lord en - du - reth for ev - er,
Allegretto (𝅗𝅥=100)
Voices alone
ff Full Org.
Ped.
120
125
But the word of the Lord en - du - reth for
Voices alone
130
135
ev - er,
the word of the
the word of the Lord en - du - reth for
Org.

140
Lord en - du - reth for ev - er, for ev - er, for ev - er, the word of the
the word of the Lord en - du - reth for ev - er, en - du - reth
the word of the
ev - er, en - du - reth for ev - er, the word of the Lord en - du - reth for
145
Lord, en - du - reth for ev - er, en - du - reth for ev - er, for ev -
for ev - er, for ev -
Lord, the word of the Lord en - du - reth for ev - er, the word of the
ev - er, en - du - reth for ev - er, for ev - er, the word of the Lord en -
150
- er, en - du - reth for ev - er, the word of the Lord en - du - reth for
- er, en - du - reth for ev - er, of the Lord en - du - reth for
Lord en - du - reth for ev - er, the word of the Lord en - du - reth for
- du - reth for ev - er, the word of the

155
160
ev - er, en - du - reth for ev - - - - - - - - - - - - -
ev - - - - - - - - er, en - du - reth for ev - er, for ev -
ev - - - - - - - - er, en - du - reth for ev - - - - - -
Lord en - du - reth for ev - er, en - du - reth for ev - - - - - -
165
- - - - er - more, en - du - reth for ev - - - er - more, for ev - er,
- - er - more, for ev - - er - more, for
- - - - er - - more, en - du - reth for ev - - er - more, for
- - - er - - more, en - du - reth for ev - - - er - more, for ev - er,
170
175
ev - - - - er - - - more. A - - - - men, A - men.
ev - - - - - er - more. A - - - - men, A - men.
ev - - - er - - - more. A - - - - men, A - men.
ev - - - - - er - more. A - - - - men, A - men.

CAST ME NOT AWAY FROM THY PRESENCE

SAMUEL SEBASTIAN WESLEY (1810-1876)

15
p
Re - store un - to me the
p
Re - store un - to
me the joy of Thy sal - va - tion,
p
Re - store un - to me the joy of Thy sal - va - tion,
- store un - to me the joy,
p
re -
BASS
p
Re - store un - to
cresc.
20
joy of Thy sal - va - tion, and up - hold me with Thy
cresc.
me the joy of Thy sal - va - tion,
cresc.
and up - hold me
- store un - to me the joy of Thy sal - va - tion,
cresc.
me the joy of Thy sal - va - tion, and up - hold me,
cresc.

Spi - rit, up - hold me, and up -
and up - hold me,
cresc.
and up - hold me,
with Thy Spi - rit, and up -
cresc.
cresc.
and up - hold me,
up - hold me, and up -
25
mf
dim.
p
- hold me with Thy Spi - rit. The
and up - hold me with Thy Spi - rit. The
up - hold me with Thy Spi - rit. The
- hold me with Thy Spi - rit. The
with Thy Spi - rit. The
- hold me with Thy Spi - rit. The

30
dim.
sa - cri - fi - ces of God are a bro - - ken spi - rit; a
sa - cri - fi - ces of God are a bro - ken spi - rit; a
sa - cri - fi - ces of God are a bro - ken spi - rit; a
sa - cri - fi - ces of God are a bro - ken spi - rit; a
sa - cri - fi - ces of God are a bro - ken spi - rit; a
sa - cri - fi - ces of God are a bro - ken spi - rit; a
35
bro - ken and a con - trite heart Thou wilt not des - pise, O
bro - ken and a con - trite heart Thou wilt not des - pise,— O
bro - ken and a con - trite heart Thou wilt not des - pise,— O—
bro - ken and a con - trite heart Thou wilt not— des -
bro - ken and a con - trite heart Thou wilt not des - pise,— O
bro - ken and a con - trite heart Thou wilt not des - pise, O—

40
Più animato
God.
God.
Make me to hear
God.
pise. Make me to hear of joy and glad - - - ness,
God.
God. Make me to hear joy and
Più animato
45
Make me to hear joy, joy and glad - - -
joy and glad - ness, glad - - - ness,
of joy and glad - - - - ness,
Make me to
glad - - - ness, joy and glad - - ness,

50
cresc.
- - - - - - - - ness, joy and glad - - - - - - -
cresc.
f
joy and glad - - - - - - -
mf cresc.
Make me to hear of joy and glad - - -
to hear joy and glad - - - - - - -
hear joy and glad - - - - - - -
Make me to hear joy and glad - - - - - - -
55
dim.
- ness, that the bones which Thou hast bro - ken may re - joice,
- ness, that the bones which Thou hast bro - ken may re - joice,
- ness, that the bones which Thou hast bro - ken may re - joice,
- ness, that the bones which Thou hast bro - ken may re - joice,
- ness, that the bones which Thou hast bro - ken may re - joice, that the
- ness, that the bones which Thou hast bro - ken may re - joice,
p
dim

60
which Thou hast bro - ken may re - joice, may re - joice,
may re - joice,
which Thou hast bro - ken may re - joice, may re - joice,
may re - joice, may re - joice, may re - joice, that the
bones which Thou hast bro - ken may re - joice, may re - joice, that the
may re - joice, may re - joice,
dim.
65
70
that the bones which Thou hast bro - ken may re-
may re - joice, that the bones which Thou hast bro - ken
may re - joice, that the bones which Thou hast bro - ken
bones which Thou hast bro - ken, that the bones which Thou hast bro - ken
bones which Thou hast bro - ken, that the bones which Thou hast bro - ken
may re - joice, that the bones which Thou hast bro - ken

75
cresc.
-joice,
may re - joice,
may re - joice
may re - joice,
that the
may re - joice,
may
may re - joice,
may
mf
80
rall.
may re - joice, re - joice.
may may re - joice, re - joice.
may re - joice, re - joice.
bones which Thou hast bro - ken may re - joice.
re - joice, may re - joice.
re - joice, may re - joice.
p

THOU WILT KEEP HIM IN PERFECT PEACE

SAMUEL SEBASTIAN WESLEY (1810-1876)

15
mf 1st. and 2nd. TENORS
20
but the night is as clear as the day. The dark-ness and the light to Thee, to
25
Tempo I
mf
to Thee are both a - like.
Thee are both a - like, to Thee are both a - like.
2nd. TENOR
Thee are both a - like, to Thee are both a - like.
mf
to Thee are both a - like.
Tempo I
p Ch.
Ped. stops in
30
p
dim.
God is light, and in Him is no dark - ness, in Him is no
God is light, and in Him is no
God is light, and in Him is no dark -
God is light, and in Him is no dark
God is light, and in Him is no
dim.
Man.
Ped.
Ch. coup.

35
cresc.
dark-ness at all. O let my soul
cresc.
dark - ness at all. O let my soul
cresc.
- - ness at all. O let my soul live,
cresc.
- - ness at all. O let my soul live, and it shall praise
cresc.
dark - ness at all. Let my soul
cresc.
Ped.
40
poco accel. (𝅗𝅥 = 80)
live, and it shall praise Thee.
mf
live, it shall praise Thee, for Thine, Thine is the king - dom, the
mf
and it shall praise Thee, for Thine is the king - dom, the
mf
Thee, shall praise Thee, for Thine is the king - dom, the
mf
live, and it shall praise Thee, for
poco accel. (𝅗𝅥 = 80)
mf
Gt. Open Diap.
Ped 16 ft
Gt. to Ped.

45
f
for Thine is the king-dom, the pow-er, and the
cresc.
pow-er, and the glo - ry, for ev - - - - - - - - -
cresc.
pow-er, and the glo - - - - - - - - - - -
cresc.
pow-er, and the glo - ry, for ev - - - - - - - - - -
cresc.
Thine is the king-dom, the pow-er, and the glo - - - - - - -
cresc.
50
dim.
p
Tempo I
glo - ry for ev - - - - - er - more.
dim.
p
- - - - - - - - - - - - er - more.
dim.
p
- - - - - - - - - - ry, for ev - er - more.
dim.
p
- - - - er - more, ev - - - er - more.
p
- - ry, for ev - - - - - - - - er - more.
Tempo I
dim.
p

55
p
Thou wilt keep him in per - fect peace, whose mind is stay -
Thou wilt keep him in per - fect peace,
Thou wilt keep him in per - - - - fect peace, whose
Thou wilt keep him in per - fect peace, whose mind, is
Thou wilt keep him in per - fect peace, whose
Ch.
p or Sw.
16 ft. in
Man.
60
dim.
p e sostenuto
rit.
65
- - ed on Thee, on Thee, is stay - - ed on Thee.
whose mind is stay - ed on Thee, is stay - - ed on Thee.
mind is stay - ed on Thee, is stay - - ed on Thee.
stay - - - ed on Thee, is stay - - ed on Thee.
mind is stay-ed on Thee, is stay - - ed on Thee.
p sostenuto
Ped. 16 ft.

WASH ME THROUGHLY FROM MY WICKEDNESS

SAMUEL SEBASTIAN WESLEY (1810-1876

20
25
all my sin, wash me through - ly from my wick-ed-ness, and for -
- give — me all — my sin, — and for - give, for - give, for -
all my sin, — wash me through - ly, and for - give, for -
all — my sin, all my sin, and for - give me
p
(cresc.)
30
- give — me all my sin, all, all my sin.
- give me all my sin, all my sin, all my sin.
- give — me all my sin, and for - give — me all, — all, all my sin.
all my sin, and for - give — me all my sin.
35
mf
For I ac - know - - - ledge my
(mf)

40
45
mf
For I ac - know - - ledge my faults, and my
faults, and my sin is ev - er be - fore me, my sin,
50
mf
For I ac - know - - ledge my faults, and my sin is
sin is ev - er be - fore me, my sin is
mf
for I ac - know - - ledge my faults, and my
55
mf
For I ac - know - - ledge my faults,
ev - - er be - fore me, for I ac -
ev - er be - fore me,
sin, my sin, I ac - know - ledge my faults, and my

60
dim.
65
I ac - know - ledge my faults.
- know - - - - ledge my faults,
I ac - know - - ledge my faults. Wash me through - ly
sin is e - - ver be - fore me.
70
mf
Wash me
from my wick - ed - ness, and for - give me all my sin.

75
cresc.
through - ly from my wick-ed-ness, and for - give me all my
mf
cresc.
For I ac - know - - - ledge my faults, my faults, my
mf
cresc.
For I ac - know - - - ledge my faults, ac - know-ledge my
cresc.
Wash
cresc.
80
sin, and for -
faults. Wash me through - ly from my wick-ed - ness, and for -
p
faults. Wash me, and for -
p
me, wash me, and for -
p

85
cresc.
p
90
cresc.
- give me all my sin, and for - give me all
- give me all my sin, and for - give me all
- give me all my sin, and for - give me all
- give me all my sin, and for - give me all
cresc.
p
cresc.
95
100
p
my sin, and for - give me all my sin.
my sin, and for - give me all my sin.
my sin, and for - give me all my sin.
my sin, and for - give me all my sin.
p

TE DEUM LAUDAMUS

HENRY SMART (1813 - 187

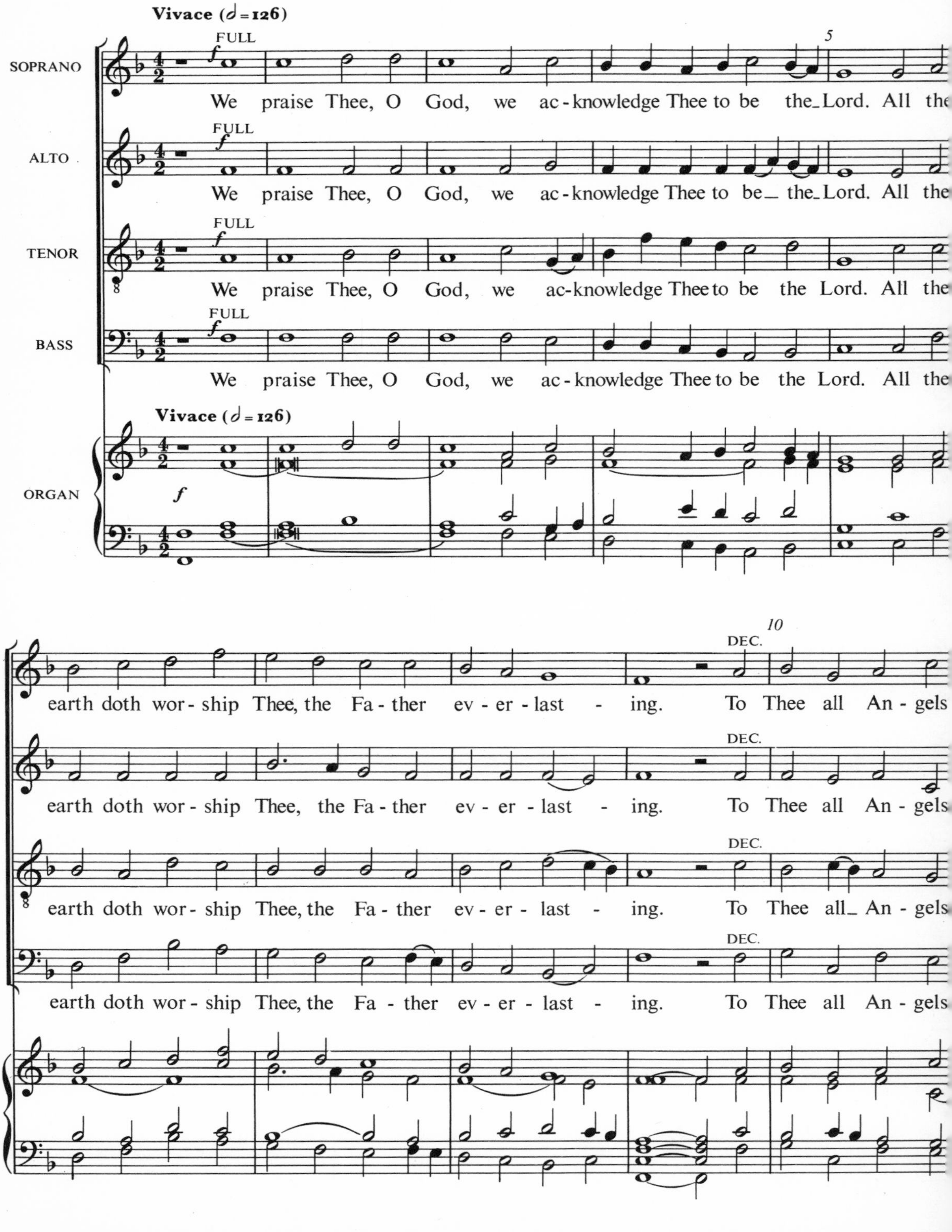

CAN.
15
cry a - loud, the Heav'ns and all the Pow'rs there-in. To Thee Che-ru-bin and Ser - a - phin con-
cry a - loud, the Heav'ns and all the Pow'rs there-in. To Thee Che-ru-bin and Ser - a - phin con-
cry a - loud, the Heav'ns and all the Pow'rs there - in. To Thee Che-ru-bin and Ser - a - phin con-
cry a - loud, the Heav'ns and all the Pow'rs there - in. To Thee Che-ru-bin and Ser - a - phin con-
FULL
20
-tin - ual - ly do cry, Ho - ly, Ho - ly,
-tin - ual - ly do cry, Ho - ly, Ho - ly,
-tin - ual - ly do cry, Ho - - - ly, Ho - ly,
-tin - ual - ly do cry, Ho - ly, Ho - ly,
cresc.
f
25
Ho - ly, Lord God of Sab - a - oth; Heav'n and earth are
Ho - ly, Lord God of Sab - a - oth; Heav'n and earth are
Ho - ly, Lord God of Sab - a - oth; Heav'n and earth are
Ho - ly, Lord God of Sab - a - oth; Heav'n and earth are

30
full of the Ma - jes-ty of Thy Glo - ry.
full of the Ma - jes-ty of Thy Glo - ry.
DEC. mf
full of the Ma - jes-ty of Thy Glo - ry. The glo - rious com- pa-ny
DEC. mf
full of the Ma - jes-ty of Thy Glo - ry. The glo - rious com- pa-ny
dim.
FULL f
35
praise Thee.
praise Thee.
cresc.
CAN. mf
of the A-pos-tles praise Thee. The good-ly fel-low-ship of the Pro-phets
of the A-pos-tles praise Thee. The good-ly fel-low-ship of the Pro-phets
p
40
Thee.
praise
DEC. mf
Thee. The no-ble ar-my of Mar-tyrs praise
praise Thee.
praise
praise Thee.
praise

45
Thee. The ho - ly Church throughout all the world doth ac - know - ledge
Thee. The ho - ly Church throughout all the world doth ac - know - ledge
Thee. The ho - ly Church throughout all the world doth ac - know - ledge
Thee. The ho - ly Church throughout all the world doth ac - know - ledge
50
dim.
Thee; The Fa - ther of an in-fi-nite Ma - jes-ty; Thine hon-our-a - ble, true, and
Thee; The Fa - ther of an in-fi-nite Ma - jes-ty; Thine hon-our-a - ble, true, and
Thee; The Fa - ther of an in-fi-nite Ma - jes-ty; Thine hon-our-a - ble, true, and
Thee; The Fa - ther of an in-fi-nite Ma - jes-ty; Thine hon-our-a - ble, true, and
55
p
f
on - ly Son; Al - so the Ho - ly Ghost, the Com - fort - er. Thou art the
on - ly Son; Al - so the Ho - ly Ghost, the Com - fort - er. Thou art the
on - ly Son; Al - so the Ho - ly Ghost, the Com - fort - er. Thou art the
on - ly Son; Al - so the Ho - ly Ghost, the Com - fort - er. Thou art the
cresc.

60
65
King of Glo - ry, O Christ. Thou art the ev - er - last - ing Son of the Fa - - ther.
King of Glo - ry, O Christ. Thou art the ev - er - last - ing Son of the Fa - - ther.
King of Glo - ry, O Christ. Thou art the ev - er - last - ing Son of the Fa - - ther.
King of Glo - ry, O Christ. Thou art the ev - er - last - ing Son of the Fa - - ther.
dim.
DEC. SOPRANOS AND ALTOS IN UNISON
p
70
When Thou tookest up - on Thee to de - liv - - er man, Thou didst not ab-
DEC. TENORS AND BASSES IN UNISON
p
When Thou tookest up - on Thee to de - liv - - er man, Thou didst not ab -
p
75
CAN.
- hor the Vir - gin's womb. When Thou hadst o - ver-come the
CAN.
- hor the Vir - gin's womb. When Thou hadst o - ver-come the

80
sharp - ness of death, Thou didst o - pen the King-dom of Heav'n to all be - liev -
sharp - ness of death, Thou didst o - pen the King-dom of Heav'n to all be - liev -
FULL
85
- ers. Thou sit - test at the right hand of God, in the Glo - ry of the
FULL
- ers. Thou sit - test at the right hand of God, in the Glo - ry of the
90
Fa - ther. We be-lieve that Thou shalt come to be our Judge.
Fa - ther. We be-lieve that Thou shalt come to be our Judge.
DEC.
95
We there-fore pray Thee, help Thy ser - vants, whom Thou hast re-
DEC.
We there-fore pray Thee, help Thy ser - vants, whom Thou hast re-

100
FULL
p cresc. poco a poco
-deem - ed with Thy pre-cious blood. Make them to be
p FULL
cresc. poco a poco
-deem - ed with Thy pre-cious blood. Make them to be
cresc. poco a poco
105
num - - ber'd with Thy Saints, in glo - - ry
num - - ber'd with Thy Saints, in glo - - ry
110
ev - er - last - ing. O Lord, save Thy peo - ple, and bless Thine
ev - er - last - ing. O Lord, save Thy peo - ple, and bless Thine
115
f
her - it - age. Gov - ern them and lift them up for ev - - er.
f
her - it - age. Gov - ern them and lift them up for ev - - er.
f

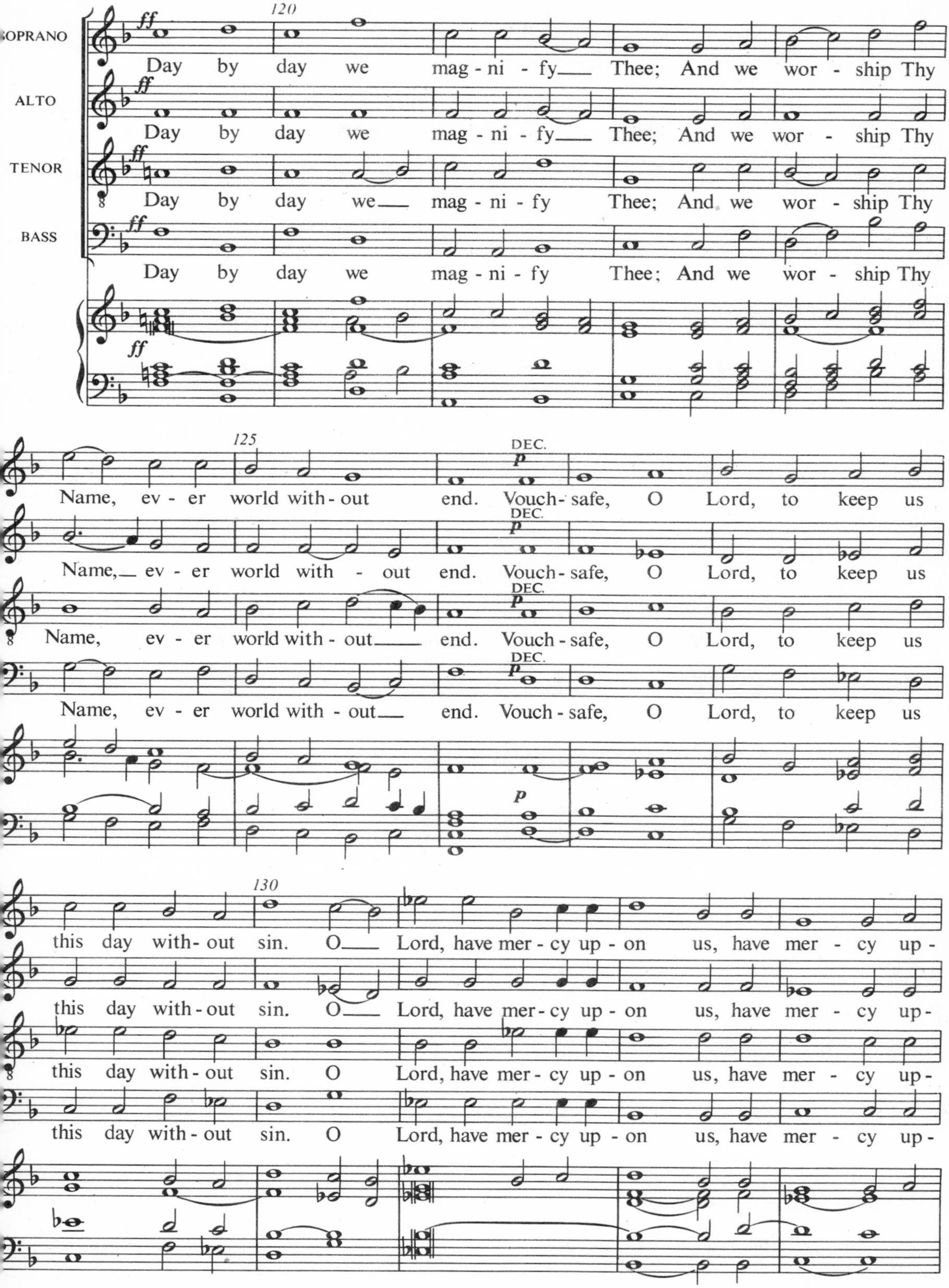
SOPRANO
ALTO
TENOR
BASS
ff
120
Day by day we mag-ni-fy Thee; And we wor-ship Thy
Day by day we mag-ni-fy Thee; And we wor-ship Thy
Day by day we mag-ni-fy Thee; And we wor-ship Thy
Day by day we mag-ni-fy Thee; And we wor-ship Thy
125
DEC.
p
Name, ev-er world with-out end. Vouch-safe, O Lord, to keep us
Name, ev-er world with-out end. Vouch-safe, O Lord, to keep us
Name, ev-er world with-out end. Vouch-safe, O Lord, to keep us
Name, ev-er world with-out end. Vouch-safe, O Lord, to keep us
130
this day with-out sin. O Lord, have mer-cy up-on us, have mer-cy up-
this day with-out sin. O Lord, have mer-cy up-on us, have mer-cy up-
this day with-out sin. O Lord, have mer-cy up-on us, have mer-cy up-
this day with-out sin. O Lord, have mer-cy up-on us, have mer-cy up-

135
CAN. (cresc.)
(dim.)
-on us. O Lord, let Thy mer - cy light - en up - on us,
(cresc.)
cresc. e rit.
140
as our trust is in Thee.
FULL a tempo
O Lord, in Thee, in
mf a tempo
145
rit.
150
Thee have I trust - ed, let me nev - er be con - found - - ed.

MAGNIFICAT AND NUNC DIMITTIS IN D MINOR

THOMAS ATTWOOD WALMISLEY (1814-1856)

1ST. SOPRANO
2ND. SOPRANO
ALTO
BASS
(mf) DEC. 15
For He hath re-gard - ed: the low - li - ness, the low - li-
(mf) CAN.
For He hath re - gard - ed: the low - li - ness, the low - li-
(mf) DEC. & CAN.
For He hath re - gard - ed: the low - li - ness, the low - li-
20
(mf) Ch.
Man.
-ness of His hand - - maid - en.
-ness of His hand - maid - en.
-ness of His hand - - maid - en.
25
FULL
f TENOR
For be - hold, from hence - forth:
f
For be - hold, from hence - forth:
f Gt to 15th.
Ped.
SOPRANO
ALTO
TENOR
BASS
30
all ge - ne - ra - tions shall call me bless - - ed.
all ge - ne - ra - tions shall call me bless - - ed.

For He that is migh - ty hath mag - ni - fied me:
For He that is migh - ty hath mag - ni - fied me:
For He that is migh - ty hath mag - ni - fied me:
For He that is migh - ty hath mag - ni - fied me:
Full Org.
Org. ad lib.
dim.
and ho - ly, ho - ly, ho - ly is His Name.
and ho - ly, ho - ly, ho - ly is His Name.
and ho - ly, ho - ly, ho - ly is His Name.
and ho - ly, ho - ly, ho - ly is His Name.
1ST. SOPRANO
2ND. SOPRANO
ALTO
BASS
DEC.
And His mer - cy is on them that fear Him: through-
CAN.
And His mer - cy is on them that fear Him: through-
DEC. & CAN.
And His mer - cy is on them that fear Him: through-
Ch.
Man.
Sw. Reed

60
65
-out all ge - - - ne - ra - tions.
-out all ge - - - ne - ra - tions.
TENOR. FULL
-out all ge - - - ne - ra - tions. He hath shew - ed strength
He hath shew - ed strength
Full Org.
Ped.
70
FULL
SOPRANO
in the i-
ALTO
in the i-
TENOR
with His arm: He hath scat - ter-ed the proud in the i-
BASS
with His arm: He hath scat-ter-ed the proud in the i-

1ST. SOPRANO
2ND. SOPRANO
ALTO
TENOR
BASS
75
DEC.
CAN.
DEC. and CAN.
-ma-gi-na-tion of their hearts. He hath put down the
-ma-gi-na-tion of their hearts. He hath put down the
-ma-gi-na-tion of their hearts. He hath put down the
-ma-gi-na-tion of their hearts.
-ma-gi-na-tion of their hearts.
p Ch.
Man.
80
85
migh-ty from their seat: and hath ex-alt-ed the hum-ble and
migh-ty from their seat: and hath ex-alt-ed the hum-ble and
migh-ty from their seat: and hath ex-alt-ed the hum-ble and

90
95
meek. He hath fill - ed the hun - gry, the hun - gry with good things:
meek. He hath fill - ed the hun - gry, the hun - gry with good things:
meek. He hath fill - ed the hun - gry, the hun - gry with good things:
Ped. p
100
105
SOPRANO
ALTO
TENOR
BASS
FULL
and the rich He hath sent emp - ty a - way.
and the rich. He hath sent emp - ty a - way.
Full to 15th.

1st time Quartet; 2nd.time Chorus
pp
110
He— re-mem-b'ring, re-mem-b'ring His mer-cy hath holp-en His ser-vant
He— re-mem-b'ring, re-mem-b'ring His mer-cy hath holp-en His ser-vant
He— re-mem-b'ring, re-mem-b'ring His mer-cy hath holp-en His ser-vant
He re-mem-b'ring, re-mem-b'ring His mer-cy hath holp-en His ser-vant
115
Is-ra-el: as— He pro-mis-ed to our— fore-fa-thers,
Is-ra-el: as— He pro-mis-ed to our— fore-fa-thers,
Is-ra-el: as He pro-mis-ed to our— fore-fa-thers,
Is-ra-el: as He pro-mis-ed to our— fore-fa-thers,

120
FULL
(f)
A - bra - ham and his seed for ev - er. Glo - ry,
A - bra-ham and his seed for ev - er. Glo - ry,
A - bra-ham and his seed for ev - er. Glo - ry,
A - bra-ham and his seed for ev - er. Glo - ry,
Full Org.
125
130
glo - ry be to the Fa - ther, and to the Son,
glo - ry be to the Fa - ther, and to the Son,
glo - ry be to the Fa - ther, and to the Son,
glo - ry be to the Fa - ther, and to the Son,

*Bass from an "Agnus Dei" from Dumont

150
and ev - - er shall be: world with-out
world with-out end. A - men, world with - out
and ev - - - er shall be: world with - out
- - - er shall be: world with - out
155
160
end, world with - out end. A - - - men, A - - men.
end. A - - - men, A - - men.
end, world with - out end. A - men, A - - men.
end. A - - - - - men, A - - men.

NUNC DIMITTIS

(𝅗𝅥 = 66)
FULL
SOPRANO
ALTO
TENOR
BASS
ORGAN
p
Lord, now lettest Thou Thy ser - - vant de-part, de - part in
peace: ac - cord - ing to Thy word. For mine eyes have
cresc.
5
10
15

20
seen Thy sal - va - - tion, Which Thou hast pre - par - ed be - fore the
seen Thy sal - va - - tion, Which Thou hast pre - par - ed be - fore the
seen Thy sal - va - - tion, Which Thou hast pre - par - ed be - fore the
seen Thy sal - va - - tion, be - fore the
25
p
face of all peo - - ple. To be a light to light - en the Gen - tiles:
face of all peo - - ple. To be a light to light - en the Gen - tiles:
face of all peo - - ple. To be a light to light - en the Gen - tiles:
face of all peo - - ple.
Man
30
35
f
and to be the glo - ry of Thy peo - ple Is - ra - el. Glo - ry
and to be the glo - ry of Thy peo - ple Is - ra - el. Glo - ry
and to be the glo - ry of Thy peo - ple Is - ra - el. Glo - ry
Glo - ry be to the Fa -
f Full to 15th.
Ped.

40
45
be to the Fa - - ther, and to the Son, and to the Ho - ly Ghost;
be to the Fa - - ther, and to the Son, and to the Ho - ly Ghost;
be to the Fa - - ther and to the Son, and to the Ho - ly Ghost;
- - - - ther, and to the Son, and to the Ho - ly Ghost;
50
As it was in the be - ginning, is now, and ev - er
As it was in the be - ginning, is now, and ev - er
As it was in the be - ginning, is now, and ev - er
As it was in the be - ginning, is now, and ev - er
Sesq. & Mixt.

*Bass of an "Amen" from Dumont

GOD IS A SPIRIT

FROM 'THE WOMAN OF SAMARIA'

WILLIAM STERNDALE BENNETT (1816-1875)

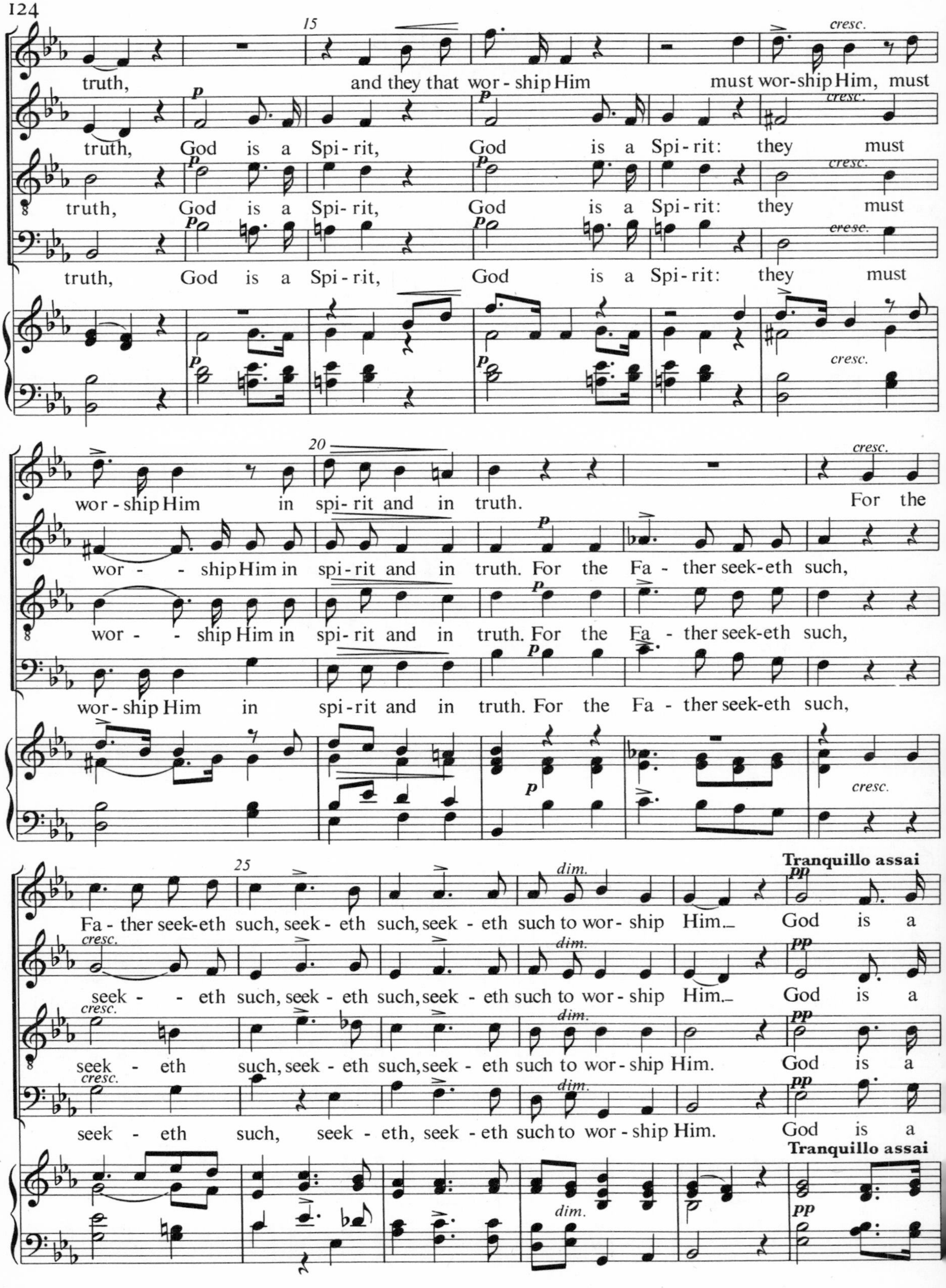
truth, and they that wor-ship Him must wor-ship Him, must
truth, God is a Spi-rit, God is a Spi-rit: they must
truth, God is a Spi-rit, God is a Spi-rit: they must
truth, God is a Spi-rit, God is a Spi-rit: they must
wor-ship Him in spi-rit and in truth. For the
wor- - ship Him in spi-rit and in truth. For the Fa - ther seek-eth such,
wor- - ship Him in spi-rit and in truth. For the Fa - ther seek-eth such,
wor-ship Him in spi-rit and in truth. For the Fa - ther seek-eth such,
Tranquillo assai
Fa - ther seek-eth such, seek - eth such, seek - eth such to wor-ship Him. God is a
seek - - eth such, seek - eth such, seek - eth such to wor-ship Him. God is a
seek - eth such, seek - eth such, seek - eth such to wor-ship Him. God is a
seek - eth such, seek - eth, seek - eth such to wor-ship Him. God is a
Tranquillo assai
cresc.
dim.
p
pp

30
35
cresc.
p
Spi-rit, God is a Spi-rit: and they that wor-ship Him, and they that wor-ship
Spi-rit, God is a Spi-rit: they that wor-ship Him, they that wor-ship
Spi-rit, God is a Spi-rit: they that wor-ship Him, they, they that wor-ship
Spi-rit: they that wor-ship Him, they that wor-ship
40
f
Him must wor-ship Him, must wor-ship Him, and they that wor-ship Him, and they that
Him must wor-ship Him, must wor-ship Him, they that wor-ship Him, must
Him must wor-ship Him, must wor-ship Him, they that wor-ship Him, must
Him must wor-ship Him, they that wor-ship Him, they must

45
sempre calando
wor- ship Him must wor-ship Him in spi-rit and in truth. The Fa - ther seek-eth such, for the
wor- ship Him, wor-ship Him in spi-rit and in truth. For the Fa - ther seek-eth such, for the
wor- ship Him, Him in spi-rit and in truth. For the Fa - ther seek-eth such, for the
wor- ship Him, Him in spi-rit and in truth. For the Fa - ther seek-eth such,
p sempre calando
50
rall.
Fa - ther seek-eth such to wor-ship Him, to wor-ship Him in spi-rit and in truth.
Fa - ther seek-eth such to wor-ship Him, to wor-ship Him in spi-rit and in truth.
Fa - ther seek-eth such to wor-ship Him, to wor-ship Him in spi-rit and in truth.
seek - eth such to wor-ship Him, to wor-ship Him in spi-rit and in truth.

IS IT NOTHING TO YOU?

Edited by
JOHN E. WEST

FREDERICK A. GORE OUSELEY (1825 - 1889)

mp
dim.
15
Be-hold, and see, be-hold, and see if there be a-ny
sor-row like un-to My sor-row, if there be
20
25
a-ny sor-row like un-to My sor-row,
a-ny sor-row like un-to My sor-row,
a-ny sor-row like un-to My sor-row,
like un-to My sor-row,

30
pp
mp
which is done un-to Me, which is done un-to Me, where-with the Lord hath af-
which is done un-to Me, which is done un-to Me, where-with the Lord hath af-
which is done un-to Me, which is done un-to Me, where-with the Lord hath af-
which is done un-to Me, which is done un-to Me, where-with the Lord hath af-
35
40
(rall.)
(pp)
-flict - ed Me in the day of His fierce an - - - - ger.
-flict - ed Me in the day of His fierce an - - - ger.
-flict - ed Me in the day of His fierce an - - - - ger.
-flict - ed Me in the day of His fierce an - - - ger.

O SAVIOUR OF THE WORLD

Edited by
HENRY G. LEY

FREDERICK A. GORE OUSELEY (1825-1889)

5
cresc.
Sa-viour of the world,— O Sa-viour of the world,— Who by Thy
Sa-viour of the world,— O Sa-viour of the world,— Who by Thy
Sa-viour of the world,— O— Sa-viour of the— world,— Who by Thy
Sa-viour of the world,— O Sa-viour of the world, Who by Thy
p
f cresc.
O Sa-viour, O Sa-viour of the world,— Who by— Thy
O Sa-viour, O Sa-viour of the— world,— Who by— Thy
O Sa-viour, O Sa-viour of the world,— Who by— Thy
O Sa-viour, O Sa-viour of the world, Who by Thy

10
dim.
cross and pre - cious blood hast re - deem - - ed
cross and pre-cious blood hast re - deem - - ed
cross and pre-cious blood hast re - deem - - ed
cross and pre - cious blood hast re - deem - - ed
cross and pre - cious blood hast re - deem - ed us, hast re-
cross and pre-cious blood hast re - deem - ed us, hast re -
cross and pre-cious blood hast re - deem - ed us, hast re-
cross and pre-cious blood hast re - deem - ed us, hast re -
f
dim.

15
us, hast re - deem - ed us: Save
us, Who hast re - deem - ed us: Save
us, Who hast re - deem - ed us: Save
us, hast re - deem - ed us: Save
- deem - ed us: Save us and help
- deem - ed us: Save us and help
- deem - ed us: Save us and help
- deem - ed us: Save us and help
pp
p
cresc.

20
mf
f
us and help us, Save us and help
us and help us, Save us and help
us and help us, Save us and help
us and help us, Save us and help
us, Save us and help us, and help
us, Save us and help us, and help
us, Save us and help us, and help us,
us, Save us and help us, and help

25
pp
us, we hum - bly be - seech Thee, O Lord.
us, we hum - bly be-seech Thee, O Lord.
us, we hum - bly be-seech Thee, O Lord.
us, we hum - bly be-seech Thee, O Lord.
us, we hum - bly be-seech Thee, O Lord.
us, we hum - bly be - seech Thee, O Lord.
help us, we hum - bly be-seech Thee, O Lord.
us, we hum - bly be-seech Thee, O Lord.
pp

REMEMBER NOW THY CREATOR

CHARLES STEGGALL (1826-1905)

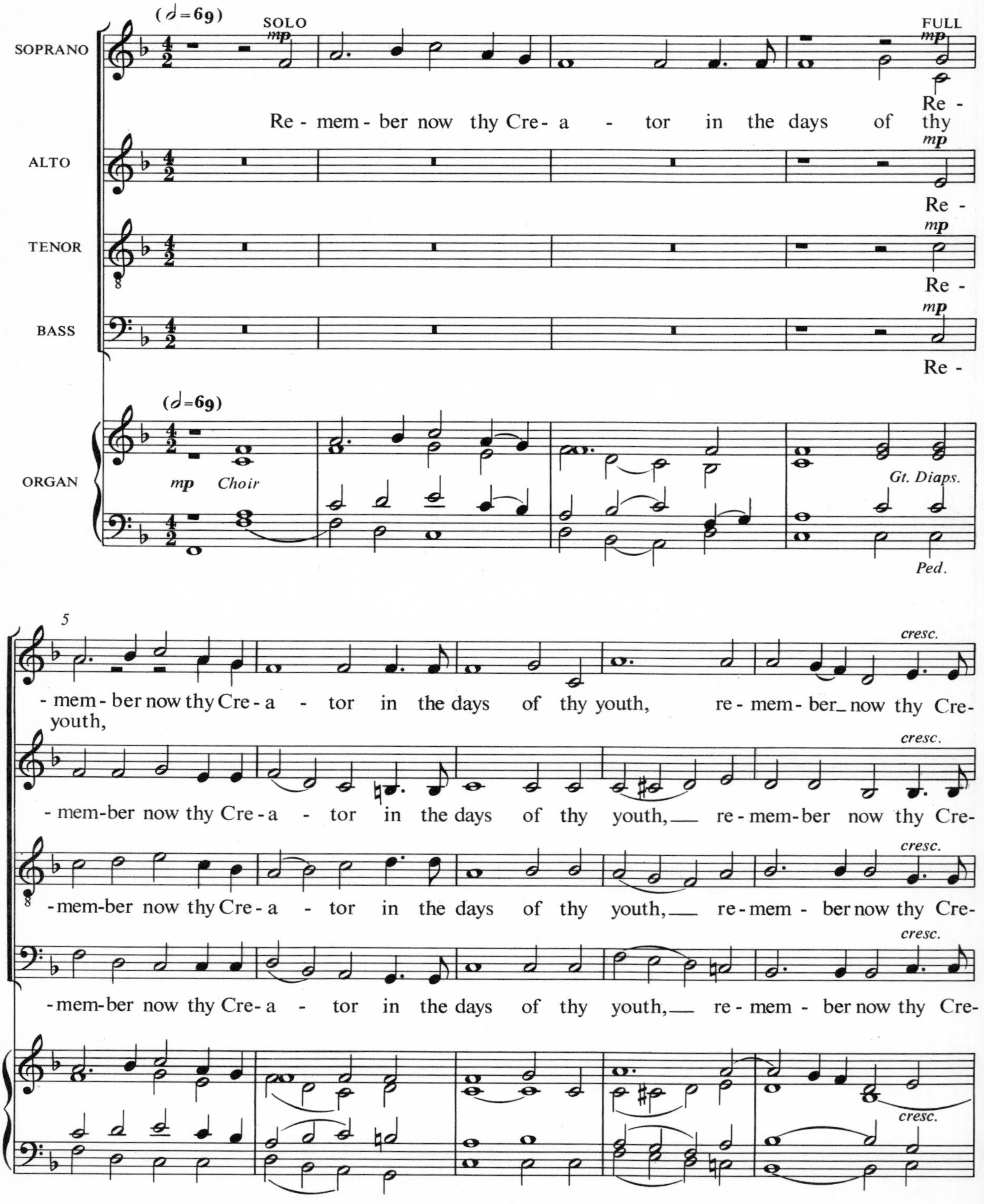

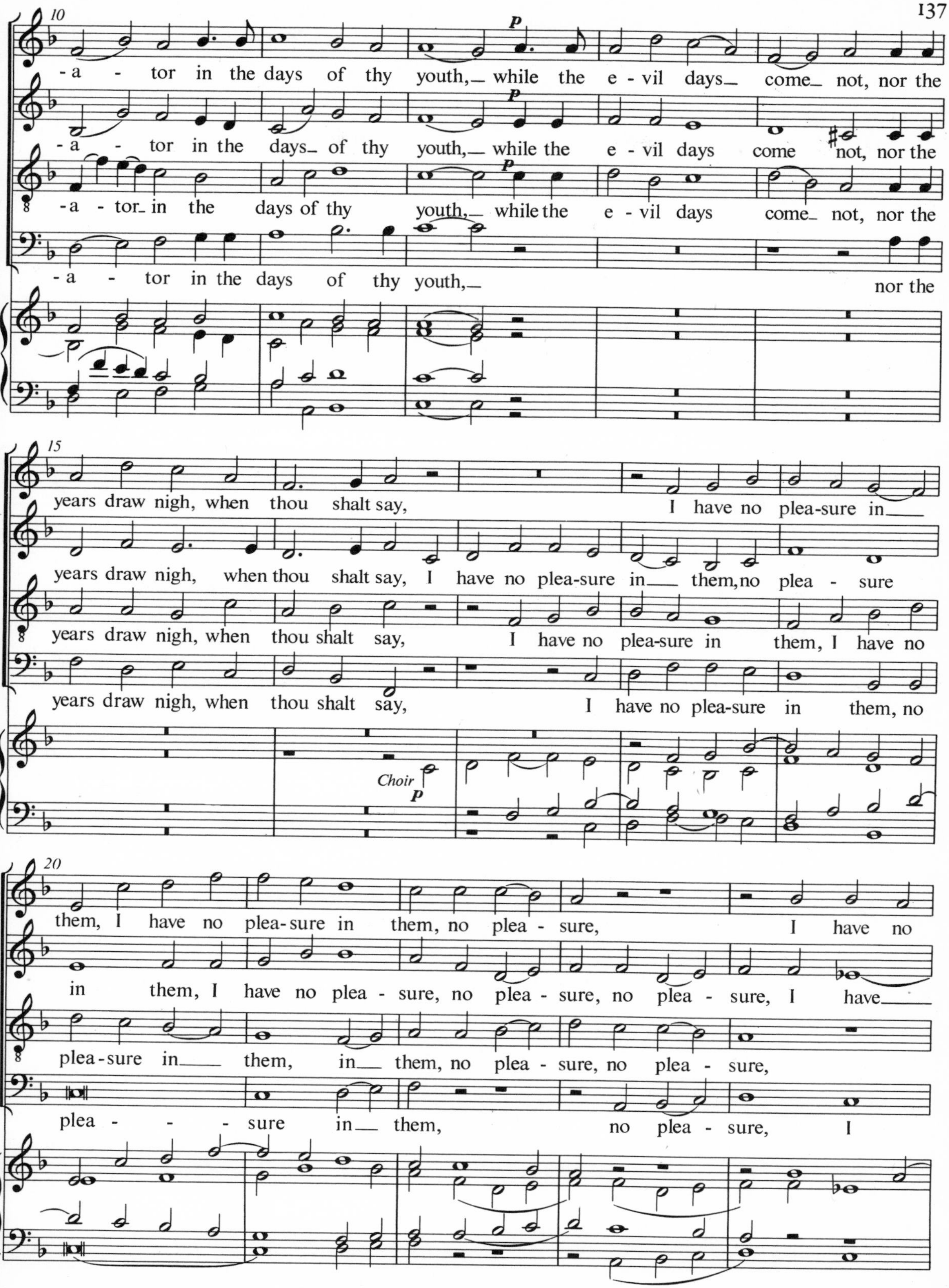
10
-a - tor in the days of thy youth,— while the e - vil days— come— not, nor the
-a - tor in the days— of thy youth,— while the e - vil days come not, nor the
-a - tor— in the days of thy youth,— while the e - vil days come— not, nor the
-a - tor in the days of thy youth,— nor the
15
years draw nigh, when thou shalt say, I have no plea-sure in—
years draw nigh, when thou shalt say, I have no plea-sure in— them, no plea - sure
years draw nigh, when thou shalt say, I have no plea-sure in them, I have no
years draw nigh, when thou shalt say, I have no plea-sure in them, no
Choir
p
20
them, I have no plea-sure in them, no plea - sure, I have no
in them, I have no plea - sure, no plea - sure, no plea - sure, I have—
plea-sure in— them, in— them, no plea - sure, no plea - sure,
plea - - sure in— them, no plea - sure, I

25
plea-sure in them.__ Re-mem-ber, re-mem-ber, re-mem-ber now thy Cre-
no plea-sure. Re-mem-ber, re-mem-ber, re-mem-ber now thy Cre-
no ple-sure. Re-mem-ber, re-mem-ber, re-mem-ber now thy Cre-
have no plea-sure.__ Re-mem-ber, re-mem-ber now thy Cre-
mp
Gt. Diaps.
30
-a-tor in the days of thy youth, re-mem-ber_ now thy Cre-a-tor in the
-a-tor in the days of thy youth,__ re-mem-ber now thy Cre-a-tor in the
-a-tor in the days of thy youth,__ re-mem-ber now thy Cre-a-tor_ in the
-a-tor in the days of thy youth,__ re-mem-ber now thy Cre-a-tor in the
35
days of thy youth,_ while the e-vil days_ come_ not, nor the years draw nigh when
days_ of thy youth,_ while the e-vil days come not, nor the years draw nigh when
days of thy youth,_ while the e-vil days come_ not, nor the years draw nigh when
days of thy youth,_ nor thy years draw nigh when
p

40
thou shalt say, I have no plea-sure in — them, I have no
thou shalt say, I have no plea-sure in — them, no plea - sure in them, I
thou shalt say, I have no plea-sure in them, I have no plea-sure in —
thou shalt say, I have no plea-sure in them, no plea - - -
Choir.
45
plea-sure in them, no plea - sure, no plea - sure, I have no plea - sure in
have no plea - sure, no plea - sure, I have no plea - sure, I
them, in — them, no plea - sure, no plea - sure, I have no plea - sure, I
- sure in — them, no plea - sure, I have no plea - sure in
Ch.
Gt.

50
rall. e dim.
them, no plea - - sure in them, I have no plea - sure in them;
have no plea - sure in them, I have no plea - sure in them;
have no plea - sure, in them, no plea - sure;
them, no plea - sure in them;
Sw.
55
p
While the sun, or the light, or the moon, or the stars, be not dark - en - ed, Nor the
Choir.

60
clouds re-turn af - ter the rain: In the day when the keep - ers of the house shall
clouds re-turn af - ter the rain: In the day when the keep - ers of the house shall
clouds re-turn af - ter the rain: In the day when the keep - ers of the house shall
clouds re-turn af - ter the rain: In the day when the keep - ers of the house shall
Gt. Diaps. 8 & 16 feet coupled to Swell
trem - ble, and the strong men shall bow them-selves, and the grind - ers cease be -
trem - ble, and the strong men shall bow them-selves, and the grind - ers cease be -
trem - ble, and the strong men shall bow them-selves, and the grind - ers cease be -
trem - ble, and the strong men shall bow them-selves, and the grind - ers cease be -
65
-cause they are few, and those that look out of the win - dows be dark - en - ed,
-cause they are few, and those that look out of the win - dows be dark - en - ed,
-cause they are few, and those that look out of the win - dows be dark - en - ed,
-cause they are few, and those that look out of the win - dows be dark - en - ed,

70
pp
And the doors shall be shut in the streets, when the sound of the grind-ing is
pp
And the doors shall be shut in the streets, when the sound of the grind-ing is
pp
And the doors shall be shut in the streets, when the sound of the grind-ing is
pp
And the doors shall be shut in the streets, when the sound of the grind-ing is
pp
75
cresc.
dim.
low, and he shall rise up at the voice of the bird, of the bird, and all the
cresc.
dim.
low, and he shall rise up at the voice of the bird, of the bird, and all the
cresc.
dim.
low, and he shall rise up at the voice of the bird, and all the
cresc.
dim.
low, and he shall rise up at the voice of the bird, and all the
Choir 8 & 4 feet

Slower
daugh - ters of mu - sic shall be brought low.
daugh - ters of mu - sic shall be brought low. Then shall the dust re -
daugh - ters of mu - sic shall be brought low. Then shall the dust re -
daugh - ters of mu - sic shall be brought low. Then shall the dust re -
Slower
Swell
80
- turn to the earth as it was,— and the spi - rit shall re-turn un-to God Who gave it.
- turn to the earth as it was,— and the spi - rit shall re-turn un-to God Who gave it.
- turn to the earth as it was, and the spi - rit shall re-turn un-to God Who gave it.

(𝅗𝅥 = 88)
85
Va - ni - ty, va - ni - ty, va - ni - ty of va - ni - ties, saith the preach - er.
Va - ni - ty, va - ni - ty, va - ni - ty of va - ni - ties, saith the preach - er.
Va - ni - ty, va - ni - ty, va - ni - ty of va - ni - ties, saith the preach - er.
Va - ni - ty, va - ni - ty, va - ni - ty of va - ni - ties, saith the preach - er.
(𝅗𝅥 = 88)
f Gt. Full
(𝅗𝅥 = 116)
90
All, all is va - ni - ty, all, all is va - ni - ty, va - ni - ty, all is
All is va - ni - ty, all, all is va - ni - ty, all, all is
All is va - ni - ty, all, all is va - ni - ty,
All, all is va - ni - ty, all, all is va - ni - ty,
(𝅗𝅥 = 116)
Ped.

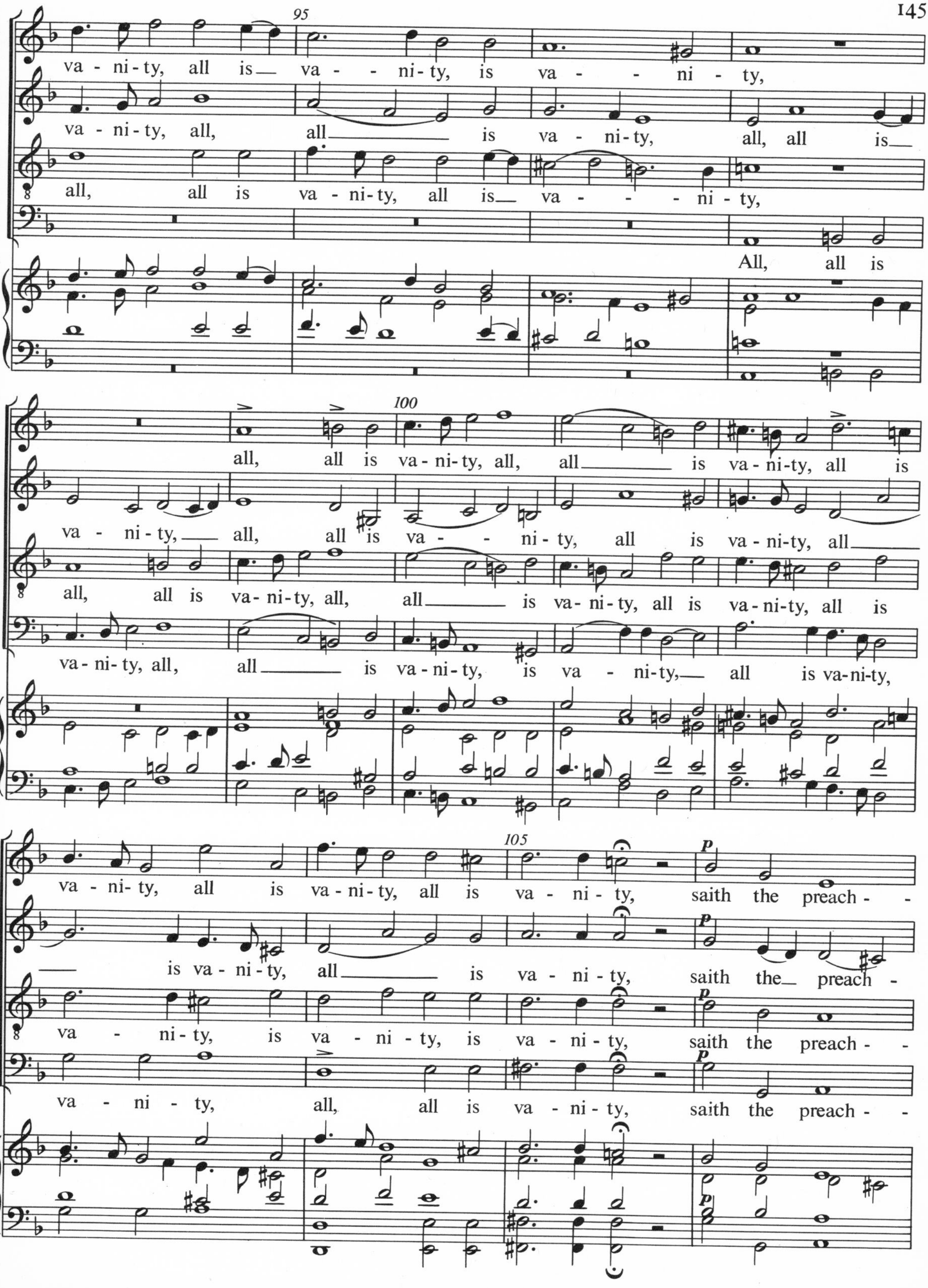
95
va - ni - ty, all is va - - ni - ty, is va - - ni - ty,
va - ni - ty, all, all is va - ni - ty, all, all is
all, all is va - ni - ty, all is va - - - ni - ty,
All, all is
100
all, all is va - ni - ty, all, all is va - ni - ty, all is
va - ni - ty, all, all is va - - ni - ty, all is va - ni - ty, all
all, all is va - ni - ty, all, all is va - ni - ty, all is va - ni - ty, all is
va - ni - ty, all, all is va - ni - ty, is va - ni - ty, all is va - ni - ty,
105
va - ni - ty, all is va - ni - ty, all is va - ni - ty, saith the preach -
is va - ni - ty, all is va - ni - ty, saith the preach -
va - ni - ty, is va - ni - ty, is va - ni - ty, saith the preach -
va - ni - ty, all, all is va - ni - ty, saith the preach -
p

mf dim. pp 110
-er, va - ni - ty of va - ni - ties, all is va - ni - ty.
-er, va - ni - ty of va - ni - ties, all is va - ni - ty.
-er, va - ni - ty of va - ni - ties, all is va - ni - ty.
-er, va - ni ty of va - ni - ties, all is va - ni - ty.
Tempo primo
SOPRANO SOLO
115
Re - mem - ber now thy Cre - a - tor in the days of thy youth, re-
Sw. p
120
-mem - ber now thy Cre - a - tor in the days of thy youth.
(poco rit.)

GOD SO LOVED THE WORLD

FROM 'THE CRUCIFIXION'

JOHN STAINER (1840-1901)

This anthem may be sung as a solo Quartet

-liev-eth in Him should not per-ish, should not per-ish, but have ev-er-
-liev-eth in Him should not per-ish, should not per-ish, but have ev-er-
-liev-eth in Him should not per-ish, should not per-ish, but have ev-er-
-liev-eth in Him should not per-ish, should not per-ish, but have ev-er-
cresc.
-last-ing life. For God sent not His Son in-to the world to con-demn the world, God
-last-ing life. For God sent not His Son in-to the world to con-demn the world, God
-last-ing life. For God sent not His Son in-to the world to con-demn the world, God
-last-ing life. God
cresc.
sent not His Son in-to the world to con-demn the world; But that the world through
sent not His Son in-to the world to con-demn the world; But that the world through
sent not His Son in-to the world to con-demn the world; But that the world through
sent not His Son in-to the world to con-demn the world; But that the world through

Him might be sav - - ed. God so loved the world,___ God
Him might be sav - - ed. God so loved the world,___ God
Him might be sav - - ed. God so loved the world,___ God
Him might be sav - - ed. God so loved the world,___ God

so loved the world,___ that He gave His on - ly be - got - ten Son, that
so loved the world,___ that He gave His on - ly be - got - ten Son, that
so loved the world, that He gave His on - ly be - got - ten Son, that
so loved the world, that He gave His on - ly be - got - ten Son, that

who - so be - liev - eth, be - liev - eth in Him should not per - ish, should not
who - so be - liev - eth, be - liev - eth in Him should not per - ish, should not
who - so be - liev - eth, be - liev - eth in Him should not per - ish, should not
who - so be - liev - eth, be - liev - eth in Him should not per - ish, should not

60
per - ish, but have ev - er - last - ing life, ev - er -
cresc.
per - ish, but have ev - er - last - ing life, ev - er - last - ing life, ev - er -
per - ish, but have ev - er - last - ing life, ev - er - last - ing life, ev - er -
per - ish, but have ev - er - last - ing life, ev - er - last - ing life, ev - er -
65
dim. e rall.
pp
70
- last - ing, ev - er - last - ing life. God so loved the world,
- last - ing, ev - er - last - ing life. God so loved the world,
- last - ing, ev - er - last - ing life. God so loved the world,
- last - ing, ev - er - last - ing life. God so loved the world,
75
ppp
rall.
God so loved the world, God so loved the world.
God so loved the world, God so loved the world.
God so loved the world, God so loved the world.
God so loved the world, God so loved the world.

HOW BEAUTIFUL UPON THE MOUNTAINS

FROM 'AWAKE, AWAKE; PUT ON THY STRENGTH, O ZION'

JOHN STAINER (1840-1901)

10
-va - tion, that pub - lish - eth peace;
ti - dings, that pub - lish - eth peace, that pub - lish - eth sal-
mf
How beau - ti - ful up-on the moun - tains are the feet of him that bringeth good
pp
that pub - lish - eth peace. How beau - ti - ful up-on the
15
- va - tion; How beau - ti - ful are the
mf
How beau - ti - ful up-on the moun - tains, how beau - ti - ful the
ti - dings, that bring - eth good ti - dings, the
20
moun - tains are the feet of him that bringeth good ti - dings,
p
feet of him that bring - eth good ti - dings, that
p
feet of him that bring - eth good ti - dings, that pub - lish - eth
p
feet of him that bring - eth good ti - dings, that bringeth good
p

p
cresc.
that pub - lish - eth peace; that saith un - to Zi - on,
pub - lish - eth peace, peace; that saith un - to Zi - on,
peace; that saith un - to Zi - on,
ti - dings of peace, good ti - dings; that saith un - to Zi - on,
25
Thy God reign - eth, that saith un - to Zi - on, Thy God reign - eth! How
Thy God reign - eth, that saith un - to Zi - on, Thy God reign - eth!
f
pp
*

* The small notes must be sung by all the parts if the passage is found too high.

30
beau - ti - ful up - on the moun - tains, How beau - ti - ful the
How beau - ti - ful up - on the moun - tains the
How
How beau - ti - ful the
senza Ped.
Ped.
feet of him that bring - eth glad
feet of him that bring - eth glad
beau - ti - ful up - on the moun - tains that bring - eth glad
feet of him, How beau - ti - ful up - on the
35
ti - dings, that pub - lish - eth peace, peace.
ti - dings, that pub - lish - eth peace, peace.
ti - dings, that pub - lish - eth peace, peace.
moun - tains, that pub - lish - eth peace, peace.
pp
rall.

YEA, THOUGH I WALK

FROM THE ORATORIO 'THE LIGHT OF THE WORLD'

ARTHUR S. SULLIVAN (1842-1900)

15
20
p
Yea, though I walk through the val - ley of the sha - dow of death, I will fear no
e - - vil, Thy rod and Thy staff com - fort me, Thy rod and staff
25
cresc.
f
com - fort me.
30
35
pp
Yea, though I walk through the val - ley of the sha - dow of death, I will
cresc.

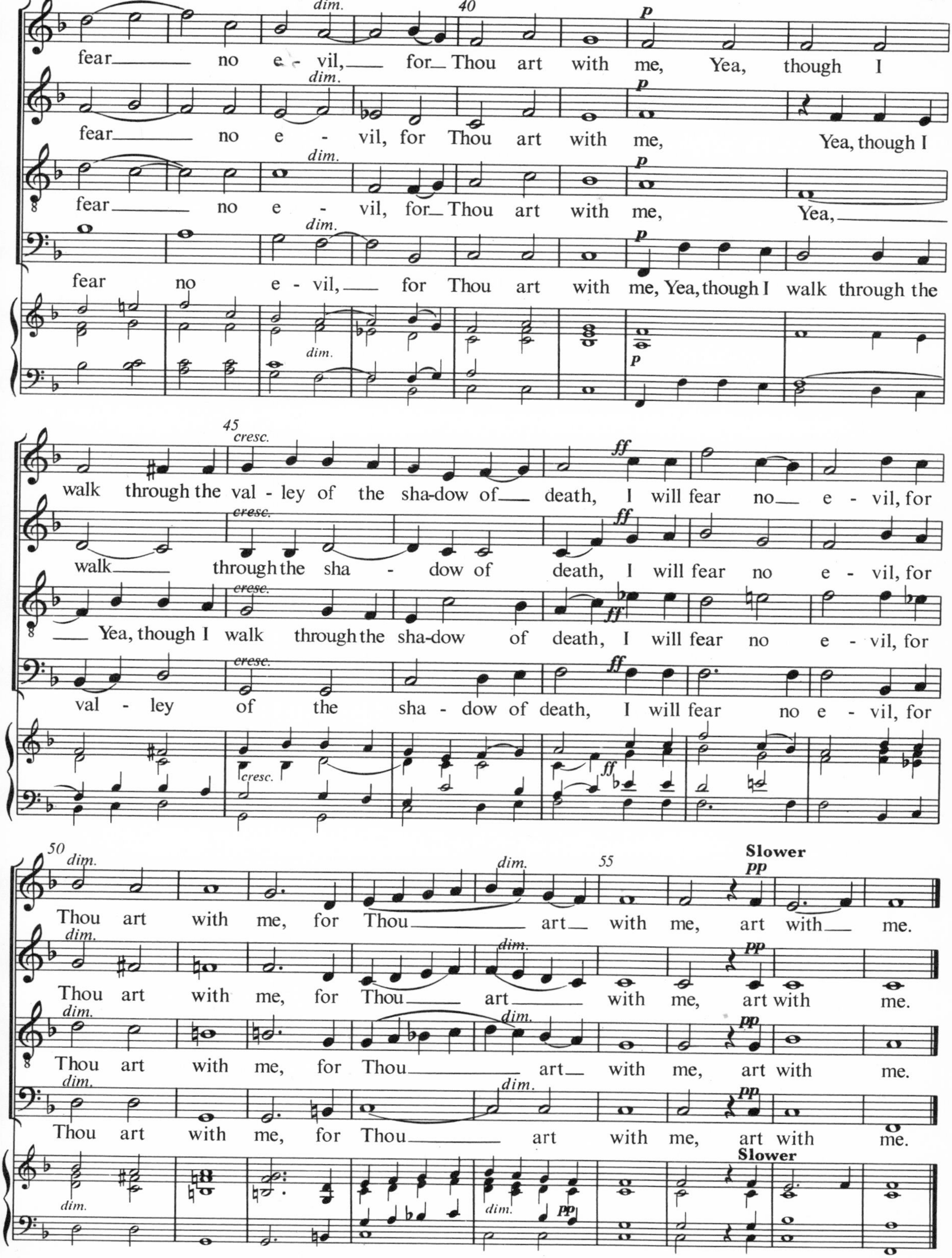
dim.
40
p
fear no e - vil, for Thou art with me, Yea, though I
fear no e - vil, for Thou art with me, Yea, though I
fear no e - vil, for Thou art with me, Yea,
fear no e - vil, for Thou art with me, Yea, though I walk through the
45
cresc.
ff
walk through the val - ley of the sha-dow of death, I will fear no e - vil, for
walk through the sha - dow of death, I will fear no e - vil, for
Yea, though I walk through the sha-dow of death, I will fear no e - vil, for
val - ley of the sha - dow of death, I will fear no e - vil, for
50
55
Slower
pp
Thou art with me, for Thou art with me, art with me.
Thou art with me, for Thou art with me, art with me.
Thou art with me, for Thou art with me, art with me.
Thou art with me, for Thou art with me, art with me.
Slower

HEAR MY WORDS, YE PEOPLE

ANTHEM FOR SOPRANO AND BASS SOLO, AND CHORUS

COMPOSED FOR THE FESTIVAL OF THE SALISBURY DIOCESAN CHORAL ASSOCIATION, 1894

C. HUBERT H. PARRY (1848-1918)

Allegro moderato

ff
15
poco rit.
SEMI-CHORUS OR QUARTET
a tempo
SOPRANO
ALTO
TENOR
BASS
f
Hear my words, ye peo-ple,
Hear my words, ye peo-ple,
Hear my words, ye peo-ple,
Hear my words, ye peo-ple,
poco rit.
a tempo
mf
mf
20
give ear unto me, give ear, give ear, all ye that have know-
give ear, give ear unto me, give ear, all ye that have
give ear unto me, all ye that have know-
give ear unto me, give ear un-to me, all ye that have

25
p
- ledge. Let us choose to us judge - ment,
know - ledge. Let us choose to us judgement, let us
- ledge. Let us choose to us judge - ment,
know - ledge. Let us choose to us judge - ment,
mf
let us choose to us judge - ment, let us know a - mong our - selves what is
choose to us judge - ment, let us know a - mong our - selves what is
let us choose to us judge - ment, let us know a - mong our - selves what is
let us choose to us judge - ment, let us know a - mong our selves what is
30
good. Be - hold, God is might - y,
good. Be - hold, God is might - y,
good. Be - hold, God is might - y,
good. Be - hold, God is might - y,

35
and de-spis-eth not a-ny, He is might-y in strength and in wis-dom.
and de-spis-eth not a-ny, He is might-y in strength and in wis-dom.
and de-spis-eth not a-ny, He is might-y in strength and in wis-dom.
and de-spis-eth not a-ny, He is might-y in strength and in wis-dom.
più f
Be-hold, He is great, and we know Him not,
Be-hold, He is great, and we know Him not,
Be-hold, He is great, and we know Him not,
Be-hold, He is great, and we know Him not,
cresc.
f
40
nei-ther can the num - ber of His years be search-ed out.
nei-ther can the num - ber of His years be search - ed out.
nei-ther can the num - ber of His years be search-ed out.
nei-ther can the num - ber of His years be search - ed out.
cresc.
ff
p

FULL CHOIR
cresc.
p
45
He is great, and we know Him not, nei - ther can the num-ber of His
He is great, and we know Him not, nei - ther can the num-ber of His
He is great, and we know Him not, nei - ther can the num-ber of His
He is great, and we know Him not, nei - ther can the num-ber of His
pp
years be search-ed out.
years be search - ed out.
years be search-ed out.
years be search - ed out.
p
mf

50
ff
The Lord's seat is in heaven,
The Lord's seat is in heaven,
The Lord's seat is in heaven,
The Lord's seat is in heaven,
cresc. molto
ff
55
the Lord's seat is in heaven.
the Lord's seat is in heaven.
the Lord's seat is in heaven.
the Lord's seat is in heaven.
Allegro energico
60
BASS SOLO
f
Clouds and darkness are
f

65
round ——— a - bout Him, Righteousness and judgement, right-eous-ness and
mf
p
judgement are— the ha - bi - ta - tion of His seat. He deck-eth Him-self with
f
70
cresc.
p
light ——— as with a gar - ment, and spread - - -
p
p cresc.
75
- - - eth out the heavens ——— like a cur - tain.
p
80
mf
He lay - - - eth the beams ——— of His
p

85
cham-bers in the wa-ters, and mak-eth the clouds His chariots, and
mf
90
mak-eth the cloud His cha-riots, and walk - eth up-on the
wings of the wind. He bow - - ed the
p
p
95
cresc.
cresc.
hea-vens, and came down, and it was dark,
cresc.
100
f
dark un-der His feet. He rode on the Che-ru-bim,
cresc.
f

105
and did fly, and came fly-ing up-on the wings of the wind,
allargando
110
rit.
and came fly - - - - - - ing up-on the wings of the
cresc.
allargando
rit.
a tempo
wind.
a tempo
115
FULL CHOIR
Sostenuto
The Lord's seat is in heaven, the Lord's seat
The Lord's seat is in heaven, the Lord's seat
The Lord's seat is in heaven, the Lord's seat
The Lord's seat is in heaven, the Lord's seat
Sostenuto
ff

120
is in heaven, His king-dom rul-eth o-ver
all.
125
f
p
Poco più mosso
130

SEMI-CHORUS OR QUARTET
135
Be - hold, the eye of the Lord is
Be - hold, the eye of the Lord is
Be - hold, the eye of the Lord is
Be - hold, the eye of the Lord is
on them that fear Him, and up-on them that put their
on them that fear Him, and up-on them that put their
on them that fear Him, and up-on them that put their
on them that fear Him, and up-on them that put their
140
trust in His mer - cy. To de - liv - er their soul from death,
trust in His mer - cy. To de - liv - er their soul from death,
trust in His mer - cy. To de - liv - er their soul from death,
trust in His mer - cy. To de - liv - er their soul from death,

145
pp
and to feed them in a time of dearth, Our soul hath pa-tient-ly
and to feed them in the time of dearth, Our soul hath
and to feed them in the time of dearth, Our soul hath pa-tient-ly
and to feed them in the time of dearth, Our soul hath pa-
p
150
tar - - - - ried for the Lord, For He, He is our help, our
pa-tient-ly tar - - ried for the Lord, For He is our help, our
tar - ried, hath tar-ried for the Lord, For He is our help, our
- tient-ly tar - - ried for the Lord, For He is our help, our
155
poco rit.
a tempo
help and our shield, our help and our shield.
help and our shield, our help and our shield.
help and our shield, our help and our shield.
help and our shield, our help and our shield.
p a tempo

SOPRANO SOLO
160
p
He de-liv-er-ed the poor in his af-flic-tion,
the fa-ther-less and him that hath none to help him.
p
He shall
165
cresc.
bind up the bro-ken-heart-ed, and proclaim li-ber-ty to the
p
cap-tives, and com-fort to those that mourn, and
p
170
rit.
a tempo
com-fort to those that mourn.
rit.
a tempo

mf
175
He shall give them beau - ty for ash - es; the gar-ment of praise for the spi - rit of
mf
hea - vi-ness, for the spi - - - rit of hea - vi-ness. For as the
180
sostenuto
earth bring-eth forth her bud, and as the gar-den caus-eth things that are
185
f
sown to spring forth. So the Lord God will cause righteousness and
rit.
a tempo
peace to spring forth be - fore all na - tions.
rit.
a tempo
p

190
Sw. Reeds
SEMI-CHORUS OR QUARTET
195
The Lord is full of com-pas-sion, is full of com-pas-sion and
mer-cy, He hath not dealt with us af-ter our sins, nor re-
200
mf
p
pp

cresc.
-ward - ed us ac-cord-ing to our wick - ed-ness, For look how high the
-ward - ed us ac-cord-ing to our wick - ed-ness, For look how high the
-ward - ed us ac-cord-ing to our wick - ed-ness, For look how high the
-ward - ed us ac-cord-ing to our wick - ed-ness, For look how high the
S.
A.
T.
B.
FULL CHOIR
pp
For
cresc.
205
heaven is in com-pa-ri-son of the earth, so great is His mer - cy
heaven is in com-pa-ri-son of the earth, so great is His mer - cy
heaven is in com-pa-ri-son of the earth, so great is His mer - cy to
heaven is in com-pa-ri-son of the earth, so great is His mer - cy to
look how high the heaven is in com - pa - ri-son of the earth,
f

210
p
— to-ward them that fear Him: Look how
— to-ward them that fear Him: Look how
-ward them that fear Him: Look how
-ward them that fear Him: Look how
mf
so great is His mer cy al - so to-ward them that fear Him,
215
f
wide al - so the east is from the west, so far
wide al - so the east is from the west, so
wide al - so the east is from the west, so
wide al - so the east is from the west, so
pp
Look how wide al - - so the east is from the west,
cresc.

dim.
hath He set our sins, hath He set our sins,
p
far hath He set our sins, hath He set our sins,
pp
so far hath He set our sins, hath He set our
p cresc.
220
our sins from us.
sins from us.

225
230
sempre cresc.
FULL CHOIR
Allegro moderato
ff
235
O praise ye the Lord, Praise_Him in the
poco rit.
240
height; Re - joice in His word Ye An - gels of Light! Ye Hea-vens a -

245
-dore Him By_ Whom ye were made, And wor-ship be-fore_ Him In bright-ness ar-
SEMI-CHORUS OR QUARTET
250
mf
O praise ye the Lord, Praise_ Him up-on earth, In tune-ful ac-
O praise ye the Lord, Praise_ Him up-on earth, In tune-ful ac-
O praise ye the Lord, Praise_ Him up-on earth, In tune-ful_ ac-
O praise ye the Lord, Praise_ Him up-on earth, In tune-ful ac-
-rayed.

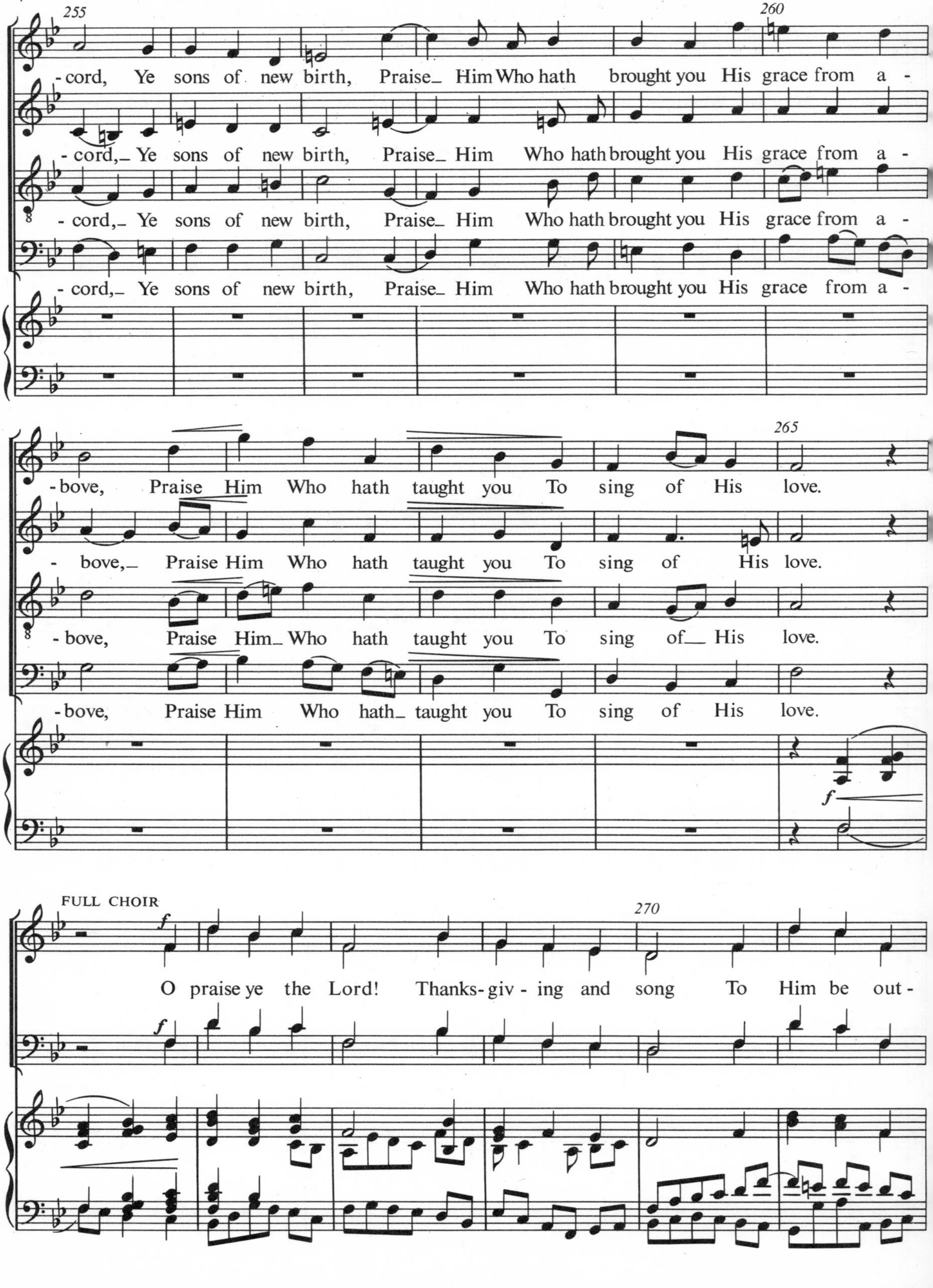
255
260
-cord, Ye sons of new birth, Praise_ Him Who hath brought you His grace from a-
-cord,_ Ye sons of new birth, Praise_ Him Who hath brought you His grace from a-
-cord,_ Ye sons of new birth, Praise_ Him Who hath brought you His grace from a-
-cord,_ Ye sons of new birth, Praise_ Him Who hath brought you His grace from a-
265
-bove, Praise Him Who hath taught you To sing of His love.
-bove,_ Praise Him Who hath taught you To sing of His love.
-bove, Praise Him_ Who hath taught you To sing of_ His love.
-bove, Praise Him Who hath_ taught you To sing of His love.
f
FULL CHOIR
f
270
O praise ye the Lord! Thanks-giv-ing and song To Him be out-
f

275
-poured All a - ges a - long; For love in cre - a - tion, For
280
Hea - ven re - stored, For grace of sal - va - tion, praise ye the
ff
SEMI-CHORUS OR QUARTET
mf
285
cresc.
A - - - - men, A -
A - - - - men, A -
A - - - - men, A -
A - - - - men, A -
Lord.
f
A - - - - - men,
f

290
A - men,
A - - - - men,
A -
- - men,
295
A - - - men, A - men, A - men.
A - men, A - men, A - - men.
A - men, A - men.
ff

TE DEUM LAUDAMUS
IN B FLAT

CHARLES VILLIERS STANFORD (1852-1924)

-last - ing.
the Heavens, and
-last - ing.
the Heavens, and
-last - ing.
To Thee all An - gels cry a - loud,
the Heavens, and
-last - ing.
To Thee all An - gels cry a - loud,
the Heavens, and
dim.
mp
all the Pow'rs therein.
To Thee Che - ru-bin and Se-ra - phin
con-
all the Pow'rs therein.
To Thee Che - ru-bin and Se-ra - phin
all the Pow'rs therein.
all the Pow'rs therein.
Sw.
Gt. coup. to Sw.
senza Ped.
Ped.
-tin - ual-ly do cry,
Ho - ly, Ho - ly,
con - tin - ual - ly do cry,
Ho - ly, Ho - ly,
con - tin - ual - ly cry,
Ho - ly, Ho - ly,
do cry,
Ho - ly, Ho - ly,
cresc.
ff

45
Ho - - ly, Lord God_ of Sa - ba - oth; Heaven and
Ho - - ly, Lord God of Sa - ba - oth; Heaven and
Ho - - ly, Lord God_ of Sa - ba - oth; Heaven and
Ho - - ly, Lord God_ of Sa - ba - oth; Heaven and
50
55
earth are full of the Ma - jes - ty of_ Thy_
earth are full of the Ma - jes - ty of_ Thy
earth are full of the Ma - jes - ty of_ Thy_
earth are full of the Ma - jes - ty of_ Thy_
60
Glo - - ry.
DEC.
p
Glo - - ry. The glo - rious com-pan-y of the A -
DEC.
p
Glo - - - ry. The glo - rious com-pan - y of the A -
DEC.
p
Glo - - - ry. The glo - rious com-pan- y of the A -
ff
dim.
p

65
CAN.
-pos-tles praise Thee. The good-ly fel-low-ship of the Prophets praise Thee.
-pos-tles praise Thee. The good-ly fel-low-ship of the Prophets praise Thee.
-pos-tles praise Thee. The good-ly fel-low-ship of the Prophets praise Thee.
70
mf FULL
DEC.
The ho-ly Church throughout
The no-ble ar-my of Mar-tyrs praise Thee. The ho-ly Church throughout
The no-ble ar-my of Mar-tyrs praise Thee. The ho-ly Church throughout
The no-ble ar-my of Mar-tyrs praise Thee. The ho-ly Church throughout
mf

75
cresc.
f
all the world doth ac - know - ledge Thee; The Fa - ther of an in-fi-nite Ma - jes- ty;
80
85
p
dim.
Thine hon - our-a - ble, true, and on - ly Son; Al - so the

90
f
Ho - ly Ghost, the Com - - - fort - er.
Thou art the
f
Ho - ly Ghost, the Com - - - fort - er.
Thou art the
f
Ho - ly Ghost, the Com - - - fort - er.
Thou art the
f
Ho - ly Ghost, the Com - - - fort - er.
Thou art the
f
95
King of Glo - ry, O Christ.
Thou art the
King of Glo - ry, O Christ.
Thou art the
King of Glo - ry, O Christ.
Thou art the
King of Glo - ry, O Christ.
Thou art the

100
ev - er - last - - ing Son of the Fa - ther.
ev - er - last - - ing Son of the Fa - ther.
ev - er - last - - ing Son of the Fa - ther. When Thou
ev - er - last - - ing Son of the Fa - ther. When Thou
p
Sw.
105
110
took - est up - on Thee to de - liv - er man, Thou didst not ab - hor the
took - est up - on Thee to de - liv - er man, Thou didst not ab - hor the
115
Vir - gin's womb. When Thou hadst o - ver - come the sharp -
Vir - gin's womb. When Thou hadst o - ver - come the sharp -
cresc.
dim.

120
125
f
the King - dom of Heaven to
the King - dom of Heaven to
-ness of death, Thou didst o - pen the King-dom, the King - dom of Heaven to
-ness of death, Thou didst o - pen the King-dom, the King - dom of Heaven to
130
all be - liev - - - - - ers. Thou sit-test at the right
all be - liev - - - - - ers. Thou sit-test at the right
135
140
hand of God, in the Glo - - - - ry of the

145
Fa - ther. We be - lieve that Thou shalt come to be our Judge.
p
32 ft.
32 ft. off.
150
155
SOLO
We there-fore pray Thee, help Thy ser - vants, whom Thou
pp
160
165
hast re - deem - ed with Thy pre - cious blood. Make them to be

170
175
num - ber'd with Thy Saints in glo - - ry ev - er -
num - ber'd with Thy Saints in glo - ry ev - er -
num - ber'd with Thy Saints in glo - ry
num - ber'd with Thy Saints in glo - - ry
CHORUS
180
p
- last - - - ing. O Lord, save Thy peo - ple,
- last - - - ing. O Lord, save Thy peo - ple,
ev - er - last - ing. O Lord, save Thy peo - ple,
ev - er - last - ing. O Lord, save Thy peo - ple,
185
190
and bless Thine he - - ri - tage. Go - vern
and bless Thine he - - ri - tage. Go - vern
and bless Thine he - - ri - tage. Go - vern
and bless Thine he - - ri - tage. Go - vern

195
200
them, and lift them up for ev - - - - - - er.
them, and lift them up for ev - - - er.
them, and lift them up for ev - - - - - - er.
them, and lift them up for ev - - - er.
205
Day by day, we mag - ni-fy Thee; And we wor - ship, we wor - ship Thy
Day by day, we mag - ni-fy Thee; And we wor - ship, we wor - ship Thy
Day by day, we mag - ni-fy Thee; And we wor - ship, we wor - ship Thy
Day by day, we mag - ni-fy Thee; And we wor - ship, we wor - ship Thy
210
Name, ev - er world with-out end, ev - er world with - out end.
Name, ev - er world with-out end, ev - er world with - out end.
Name, ev - er world with-out end, ev - er world with - out end.
Name, ev - er world with-out end, ev - er world with - out end.

215
220
p
Vouch-safe, O Lord, to keep us this day with - out
Vouch-safe, O Lord, to keep us this day with - out
p
O Lord, have mer - - - - cy up - on
225
O Lord, have mer - cy up - on us, have mer - cy up-
sin.
O Lord, have mer - cy up - on us, have mer - cy up-
230
cresc.
us. O Lord, let Thy
- on us. O Lord, let Thy
- on us. O Lord, let Thy mer - - - - -
- on us. O Lord, let Thy

mer - cy light - en up - on us, as our trust is in
mer - cy light - en up - on us, as our trust is in
- cy light - en up - on us, as our trust is in
mer - cy light - en up - on us, as our trust is in
Thee. O Lord, in Thee have I trust - ed:
Thee. O Lord, in Thee have I trust - ed: let me nev -
Thee. O Lord, in Thee have I trust - ed: let me
Thee. O Lord, in Thee have I trust ed:
let me nev - - - er be con - found - - - - ed.
- er be con - found - - - ed.
nev - er be con - found - - - - - ed.
let me nev - er be con - found - - - - ed.

NUNC DIMITTIS
IN B MINOR

T. TERTIUS NOBLE (1867-1953)

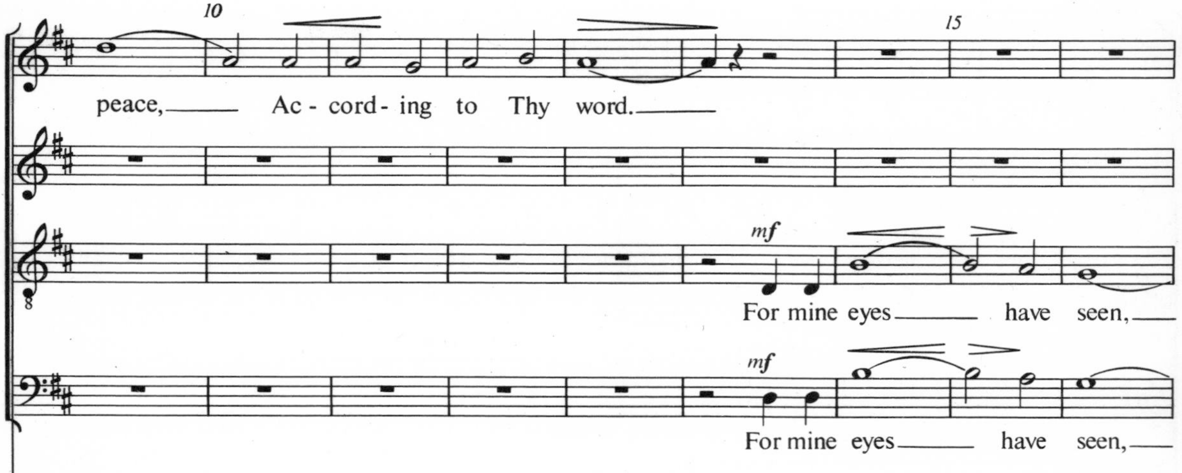

20
25
mf
Which Thou hast pre-par-ed be-
Which Thou hast pre-par-ed be-
have seen Thy sal-va-tion, Which Thou hast pre-par-ed be-
have seen Thy sal-va-tion, Which Thou hast pre-par-ed be-
30
35
-fore the face of all peo-ple; To be a light to light-
-fore the face of all peo-ple; To be a light to light-
-fore the face of all peo-ple; To be a light to light-
-fore the face of all peo-ple;

40
45
f
dim.
-en the Gen - tiles, and to be the glo - - - ry of Thy peo - ple,
and to be the glo - - - ry of Thy peo - ple,
50
Maestoso
f a tempo
55
Thy peo - ple Is - - ra - el. Glo - ry be to the Fa - ther, and
Thy peo - ple Is - ra - el. Glo - ry be to the Fa - ther, and
Maestoso
f a tempo

60
to the Son, and to the Ho - ly Ghost; As it was in
Full Sw. closed
f Gt. Org.
65
70
the be - gin - ning, is now, and ev - er shall be, world with - out

75
80
f
end. A - - - men, world with - out
85
90
poco rall.
end. A - - - men, A - - - - - men.

First page of the MS. score of Walmisley's Magnificat in D minor, in the composer's hand, from York Minster Library

(by kind permission of the Dean and Chapter)

NOTES ON THE MUSIC

BENJAMIN COOKE: **Magnificat from the Evening Service in G**
Cooke was born in London in 1734 and died there on September 14th, 1793. For most of his professional life he was organist at Westminster Abbey, where he is buried. He wrote a great quantity of music (including many glees), but little is published. There is a tradition that the Service in G was written for the enlarged organ at the Abbey. A pedal organ had been added some time in 1778, probably in the spring, as the date at the end of the manuscript of the Evening Service, now in the Library of the Royal College of Music, is July 31st, 1778. (For further information about the Abbey organ see 'The Organs and Bells of Westminster Abbey' by Jocelyn Perkins; Novello, 1937). The small bass notes in bars 40–43 and 76–78, intended no doubt to show off the new pedal organ, are added to the original manuscript in a later hand. Despite its rather obvious rhythms and word repetition the Service still retains a certain popularity.

JONATHAN BATTISHILL: **O Lord, look down from heaven**
Battishill was born in London in May 1738 and died there on December 10th, 1801. He became a chorister at St. Paul's Cathedral at the age of nine. In 1764 he was appointed organist of St. Clement, Eastcheap and St. Martin, Ongar, and in 1767 organist of Christ Church, Newgate Street. Apart from his anthems and chants he wrote music for the theatre (he was harpsichordist at Covent Garden).

O Lord, look down from heaven was written with the acoustics of St. Paul's Cathedral in mind. Note the rests in bars 71 and 83; as a composer of music for the theatre he would naturally think of his audience. Other effective features of this anthem are the repetition of 'Thy zeal' in bars 34ff., which is not just monotonous but produces a really dramatic climax; the long dominant pedal beginning at bar 92; the second sopranos reinforcing the firsts on their high G at bar 100; and the alto and tenor passage at bars 105–6. This anthem should always be sung with organ accompaniment to achieve an historically correct performance.

SAMUEL ARNOLD: **Nunc dimittis from the Evening Service in A**
Arnold was born in London on August 10th, 1740, and died there on October 22nd,

1802. He was a prolific composer of oratorios, operas and pantomimes, as well as of odes, services and anthems. In 1783 he gained his D.Mus. at Oxford and in the same year succeeded James Nares as composer to the Chapel Royal. In 1786 he began an edition of Handel's works that ran to 36 volumes. In 1790 he produced an important work, *Cathedral Music*, in four volumes ('being a collection in score, of the most valuable and useful Compositions for that Service by the several English masters of the last Two Hundred Years'), as a continuation of Boyce's work of the same name. In 1793 he succeeded Benjamin Cooke as organist of Westminster Abbey. He is buried there, near to Purcell and Blow.

The Evening Service in A was written to complete Boyce's Morning and Ante-Communion Service in the same key. This straightforward, uneventful music was staple fare for the Cathedral choirs of the time, which is a commentary on the un-ambitious level of the Church music then in use. The final cadence (bars 35–36) has a certain interest, with its low tenor part and the omission of the fifth in the final bar of the voice parts.

THOMAS ATTWOOD: **Come, Holy Ghost**
Turn Thy face from my sins

Attwood was born in London on November 23rd, 1765, and died there on March 24th, 1838. He became a chorister of the Chapel Royal at the age of nine. At the age of sixteen he performed before the Prince of Wales (later George IV), through whose interest he was sent abroad to study, first to Naples and then to Vienna, where he became a pupil of Mozart. He returned to England in 1787 and from that time played an important part in the English musical scene. He became music tutor to the Duchess of York and the Princess of Wales, and in 1796 organist of St. Paul's Cathedral. He was one of the founders of the London Philharmonic Society in 1813, and on the foundation of the Royal Academy of Music in 1823 became a professor there. In 1836 he became organist at the Chapel Royal. He was an enthusiastic supporter of Mendelssohn when he first appeared before the English musical public. He is buried in St. Paul's Cathedral.

He wrote a large number of operas, thirty-two in all, but later in life devoted him-self to Church music. He wrote the Coronation anthems for George IV *(I was glad)* and William IV *(O Lord, grant the King a long life)*. The two anthems included in this volume show him as a composer with a melodic gift, who could produce agreeable, gracious and not very original music.

SAMUEL WESLEY: **Sing aloud with gladness** *(Exultate Deo)*

Samuel Wesley was born in Bristol on February 24th, 1766, and died in London on October 11th, 1837. He was the son of Charles Wesley, the hymn writer (1707–1788) and nephew of John Wesley, the founder of Methodism (1703–1791). He was a prodigy whose musical gifts were fostered by his brother Charles (1757–1834), himself an excellent organist and harpsichordist. He began composing at the age of eight and already in 1777 his *Eight Lessons for the Harpsichord* were published. As an organist he enjoyed the reputation of being the greatest performer and improviser of his day. In 1784 he joined the Roman Catholic Church, and composed several motets to Latin words. He was devoted to the music of J. S. Bach and did much to spread knowledge of it in England. In this connection he published his edition of Bach's 'Well-tempered Clavier' in 1813.

The motet here represented is an excellent example of his contrapuntal style. Note the syncopated rhythms at bars 231ff., avoiding a square pattern; also the interesting modulations throughout the piece. The motet was probably sung unaccompanied originally. The tradition at St. George's Chapel, Windsor, was to sing it unaccompanied and then for the organ to play the final instrumental passage—a dangerous procedure at times!

WILLIAM CROTCH: **Lo, star-led chiefs (from 'Palestine')**

Crotch was born in Norwich on July 5th, 1755, and died at Taunton on December 27th, 1847. There is an account given by Charles Burney (1726–1814) that he played on a small organ at the early age of two and a half. Such precocity, however, did not mature into a great talent for composition. In 1779 he made his first public London appearance. Then when only eleven, he went to Cambridge and became assistant to the Professor of Music, Dr. Randall, and organist of both Trinity and King's Colleges, as well as of Great St. Mary's Church. In 1788 he proceeded to Oxford and studied for the Ministry for two years, during which time his oratorio *The Captivity of Judah* was composed (1789). In 1790 he became organist of Christ Church, Oxford, and in 1797 succeeded Philip Hayes (1738–1797) as Professor of Music in the University. He was appointed Principal of the newly-founded Royal Academy of Music in 1822.

The oratorio *Palestine* was written in 1812. The excerpt printed in this volume was originally intended to be sung by a solo quartet. It was one of the few pieces used as an Epiphany anthem in the Church repertoire of the time. The fine Tudor examples had not yet come to light.

JOHN GOSS: **If we believe that Jesus died**
O Saviour of the world

Sir John Goss was born at Fareham on December 27th, 1800, and died in London on May 10th, 1880. He entered the Chapel Royal as a boy chorister, became a pupil of Thomas Attwood and after various organ posts was elected as organist of St. Paul's Cathedral after the death of Attwood in 1838. He held that position until 1872, the year of his knighthood. His Church music includes services, many anthems, chants, psalms, hymns and carols. He also edited a collection of hymns, a Chant book and a *Church Psalter and Hymn Book*. His textbook *An Introduction to Harmony and Thorough-bass* went through several editions.

His music is clear and wholesome. Its diatonic character is refreshing at a time when chromaticism was in vogue. *If we believe that Jesus died* was written for the funeral service of the Duke of Wellington in 1852. Its excellent dramatic qualities were well suited to the occasion and to the acoustics in St. Paul's Cathedral. Noteworthy are the seventh leaps of the bass in bar 33 and of the tenor in bar 35; the change to the major in bar 64; and the effective build-up from bar 70. The composer intended this anthem to be sung with accompaniment throughout.

O Saviour of the world is much simpler in texture and in intention, but there are some shrewd harmonic touches in bars 18–23 and bar 44. The accompaniment provides a contrasting colour to that of the voices, and should never be omitted. The *sforzandi* should not be overdone in performance.

SAMUEL SEBASTIAN WESLEY: **Blessed be the God and Father**
Cast me not away from Thy presence
Thou wilt keep him in perfect peace
Wash me throughly from my wickedness

S. S. Wesley was born in London on August 14th, 1810, and died at Gloucester on April 19th, 1876. He was a boy chorister at the Chapel Royal, after which he held appointments in several London churches as organist. In 1832 he became organist of Hereford Cathedral; in 1835, of Exeter Cathedral; in 1842, of Leeds Parish Church; in 1849, of Winchester Cathedral; and in 1865, of Gloucester Cathedral.

His works include four Church services and twenty-seven anthems. His famous publication, *A Few Words on Cathedral Music and the Musical System of the Church, with a Plan of Reform*, appeared in 1849. Spohr wrote of S. S. Wesley: 'His sacred music is chiefly distinguished by a noble, often even an antique, style, and by rich harmonies as well as by surprisingly beautiful modulations'. He had a genuine melodic gift and this, combined with his judicious use of discords and double or triple suspensions results in works that are 'universally recognised as standard works of excellence'. Examples of his fine melodies are to be found in *Let us lift up our heart* (the solo passage in the second movement of *Thou, O Lord God, art the thing that I long for*); *Say to them that are of a fearful heart* (from *The Wilderness*); and the soprano solo *My voice shalt Thou hear betimes, O Lord* (from *Praise the Lord, O my soul*).

Blessed be the God and Father was composed in 1853. There is a story that *Cast me not away from Thy presence* was written at a time when Wesley had broken his leg, hence the special significance of bars 55ff.! Note the effective use of suspensions in *Thou wilt keep him in perfect peace*, especially in the closing cadence from bar 62. In *Wash me throughly from my wickedness* note the colourful turns of harmony, the fine dramatic build-up from the appearance of the second theme in bar 37 and the combination of the first and second themes at bars 73ff.

HENRY SMART: **Te Deum in F**

Henry Smart was born in London on October 26th, 1813, and died there on July 6th,

1879. He was the nephew of Sir George Smart (1776–1867), who as conductor of the London Philharmonic Society's concerts did much to introduce the works of Beethoven and Schumann to England. He held various organists' posts in London, his last being at St. Pancras, Euston Road. Towards the end of his life he became blind. He wrote many anthems, besides a full Morning, Communion and Evening Service in F, and Evening Services in B flat and G.

The *Te Deum*, which forms part of this, is not great music, yet is still fresh and effective. The rhythmic squareness of the music on paper should not prevent a good choir with careful phrasing from producing a tasteful result. The voices in unison at bar 67ff. contrast well with the organ accompaniment; the build-up at bar 100ff. is well contrived; and there are some effective modulations.

THOMAS ATTWOOD WALMISLEY: **Magnificat and Nunc dimittis in D minor**

Walmisley was born in London on January 21st, 1814, and died at Hastings on January 17th, 1856. His father, Thomas Forbes Walmisley (1783–1866), had studied with Thomas Attwood, and the latter became godfather to the young Walmisley. He too became a pupil of Attwood, and in 1830 was appointed organist of Croydon Parish Church. In 1833 he became organist of both Trinity and St. John's Colleges, Cambridge, and in 1836, at the early age of twenty-two, was elected to the Chair of Music at that University. His reputation as an organist stood very high, and he was an intimate friend of Mendelssohn. His anthems and Church services were published after his death by his father in the volume *Cathedral Music* (1857).

The Magnificat and Nunc dimittis in D minor, composed in 1855, is an outstanding work, never afterwards equalled by Walmisley and on the level of S. S. Wesley's best work. The independence of the organ accompaniment; the layout of the voices, which are variously combined almost as orchestral instruments; and the dynamic contrasts (for example, the *pp* at bar 106, followed by the sudden *f* at bar 122) are all features to be admired. The work is deservedly a classic of English Church music.

WILLIAM STERNDALE BENNETT: **God is a Spirit (from 'The Woman of Samaria')**

Sir William Sterndale Bennett was born in Sheffield on April 13th, 1816, and died in London on February 1st, 1875. In 1826 he entered the Royal Academy of Music as a student. Later he was sent abroad to study and while in Germany became an intimate friend of both Mendelssohn and Schumann (Schumann dedicated his *Etudes Symphoniques* to him). He founded the Bach Society in 1849, became Professor of Music at Cambridge University in 1856, and in 1866 was appointed Principal of the Royal Academy of Music. He was knighted in 1871. He is buried in Westminster Abbey.

Eminent in his own day, he is almost completely neglected nowadays. Of the oratorio *The Woman of Samaria* (which had an enormous vogue at that time) only *God is a Spirit* and *Abide with me* are known now, and seem trite by comparison with the works of his two German friends.

FREDERICK A. GORE OUSELEY: **Is it nothing to you?**
O Saviour of the world

Sir Frederick Arthur Gore Ouseley was born in London on August 12th, 1825, and died at Hereford on April 6th, 1889. He was the son of Sir Gore Ouseley, the British Ambassador to Persia. He studied at Oxford University and was ordained a priest in 1849. In 1855 he became Professor of Music at Oxford, and at his instigation examinations for Oxford music degrees were revived. In 1856 he founded and endowed St. Michael's College, Tenbury (with Stainer as organist) for the maintenance of the tradition and standards of English Cathedral music. It possesses a fine library, including an autograph score of Handel's *Messiah* used by the composer at the first performance in Dublin in 1742. Among his compositions are two oratorios; eleven Church services; seventy anthems; chants; and a collection of *Cathedral Services by English Masters*.

He, together with Stainer, did much to remedy the lack of liturgical music for special Church festivals and Saints' Days. The two anthems included in this volume were written for use on Good Friday. The eight-part writing in *O Saviour of the World* is unusual at a time when the standard of singing was so low and the size of the choirs were so small. Both anthems are intended to be sung unaccompanied.

CHARLES STEGGALL: **Remember now thy Creator**

Steggall was born in London on June 3rd, 1826, and died there on June 7th, 1905. He was a student at the Royal Academy of Music under Sterndale Bennett, and from 1851 to 1903 was a professor there. He edited the volume *Church Psalmody* in 1848 and a new edition of *Hymns Ancient and Modern* in 1889. *Remember now thy Creator* is a well-balanced composition (note the opening and closing section given to the soprano solo). The unison passage from bar 55ff. is dramatically effective.

JOHN STAINER: **God so loved the world**
(from 'The Crucifixion')
How beautiful upon the mountains
(from 'Awake, awake; put on thy strength, O Zion')

Sir John Stainer was born in London on June 6th, 1840, and died in Verona on March 31st, 1901. He became a chorister of St. Paul's Cathedral in 1847; held various organ appointments; was appointed organist of St. Paul's in 1872; and was knighted in 1888. The following year he became Professor of Music at Oxford University. Apart from composing he did valuable research into the music of the Middle Ages.

The Crucifixion was first produced in London in 1887. It seems strange that this work should still be so widely performed. Perhaps this simple and melodious excerpt as well as the hymns save it from the oblivion to which much present-day critical taste would consign it. *How beautiful upon the mountains* (an excerpt from a Saints' Day anthem) has a certain contrapuntal interest. It cannot be denied that for Stainer, as for most of his contemporaries, the simple and sweet melody was of chief, and the words only of secondary, importance. These could be repeated at will in order to fit into the melodic scheme, often with absurd results. For this reason it seems unlikely that the major portion of Stainer's Church music will ever be restored to use.

ARTHUR S. SULLIVAN: **Yea, though I walk (from 'The Light of the World')**

Sir Arthur Seymour Sullivan was born in London on May 13th, 1842, and died there on November 22nd, 1900. He entered the Chapel Royal as a chorister in 1852, and already in 1855 had an anthem published. In 1856 he was the first student to gain the newly founded Mendelssohn Scholarship in composition. The following years saw the production of instrumental and choral works, and it was not until 1867 that his first comic opera *(Cox and Box)* was produced. He was knighted in 1883.

Though Sullivan liked to think of himself as a serious composer, his real genius lay in his works for the theatre. *Yea, though I walk* comes from his oratorio *The Light of the World*, composed in 1873. As might be expected, the music is singable, but has very little depth. This is true of all of his Church music, much of which seems incredibly banal to us today.

C. HUBERT H. PARRY: **Hear my words, ye people**

Sir Charles Hubert Hastings Parry was born in Bournemouth on February 27th, 1848, and died at Rustington on October 7th, 1918. He was educated at Eton and Oxford, and already by 1868 had had a composition played at the Three Choirs Festival. He was appointed Choragus of Oxford University in 1883 and in 1894 succeeded Sir George Grove as Director of the recently founded Royal College of Music. He was knighted in 1898. From 1899 to 1908 he was Professor of Music at Oxford University.

His serious and refined taste is well expressed in his fine choral works, among them *Scenes from Shelley's Prometheus Unbound* (1880) and *Job* (1892), and his famous unison song *Jerusalem* is a fine example of nation-stirring song. *Hear my words, ye people*, planned on a large scale like the verse anthems of the sixteenth- and seventeenth-century composers, was written in 1894 for the Festival of the Salisbury Diocesan Choral Association. The division of forces into soloists, semi-chorus (the Cathedral choir) and full choir, as well as the excellent writing for the soprano and bass soloists, are admirable features.

(For a later example of Parry's work see **My soul, there is a country** in Volume 5.)

CHARLES VILLIERS STANFORD: **Te Deum in B flat**

Sir Charles Villiers Stanford was born in Dublin on September 30th, 1852, and died in

London on March 29th, 1924. He came to London as a piano student in 1862 and proceeded to Cambridge in 1870. From 1873 to 1902 he was organist of Trinity College there. In 1883 he became professor of composition at the Royal College of Music, and in 1887 was appointed Professor of Music at Cambridge University. He held both of these posts until his death. He was knighted in 1902.

Together with Parry he infused altogether new standards into the Church music of the day. His Te Deum, part of the Morning, Communion and Evening Service in B flat, composed in 1879, is noteworthy in its attempt to bind the composition together by the repetition of musical phrases. The opening theme is based on a plainsong melody, which was indeed a new element in late-nineteenth-century English Church music. The 'fresh wind of change' is also to be felt in the fine modulation at bar 190.

(For a later example of Stanford's work see **Beati quorum via** in Volume 5.)

T. TERTIUS NOBLE: **Nunc dimittis in B minor**

Thomas Tertius Noble was born at Bath (England) on May 5th, 1867, and died at Rockport, Mass. (U.S.A.) on May 4th, 1953. He entered the Royal College of Music in 1884, where he studied composition under Stanford. From 1890 to 1892 he was assistant organist at Trinity College, Cambridge and organist at Ely Cathedral from 1892 to 1898. He proceeded to York and was organist of York Minster until 1913. He then accepted the position of organist and choirmaster at St. Thomas' Episcopal Church in New York City, which he held until his retirement in 1947.

The Evening Service in B minor was written during his student days when his teacher Walter Parratt (1841–1924) suggested that he should write a Service in the style of Walmisley in D minor. It is a simple, diatonic setting, in contrast to the rather lush chromaticism of some of his other compositions.

REPRESENTATIVE LIST OF COMPOSITIONS

(Items printed in **bold type** are included in this Volume)

ARNOLD, SAMUEL (1740–1802)	
Magnificat and **Nunc dimittis** in A	N.
ATTWOOD, THOMAS (1765–1838)	
Come, Holy Ghost	N.
O God, who by the leading of a star	CMS.
Teach me, O Lord, the way of Thy statutes	BO.
Turn Thee again, O Lord	N.
Turn Thy face from my sins	N.
BATTISHILL, JONATHAN (1738–1801)	
Call to remembrance	N.
O Lord, look down from heaven	N.
BENNETT, WILLIAM STERNDALE (1816–1875)	
Abide with me (from 'The Woman of Samaria')	N.
God is a Spirit (from 'The Woman of Samaria')	N.
In Thee, O Lord	N.
O that I knew where I might find Him	N.
Remember now thy Creator	N.
COOKE, BENJAMIN (1734–1793)	
Morning Service in G	N.
Magnificat and Nunc dimittis in G	N.
COOKE, ROBERT (1768–1814)	
Evening Service in C	N.
CROTCH, WILLIAM (1774–1847)	
Be peace on earth	BA.
Comfort, O Lord, the soul of Thy servant	BO. N.
How dear are Thy counsels	N.
Lo, star-led chiefs (from 'Palestine')	N.

ELGAR, EDWARD (1857–1934)	
Ecce sacerdos magnus	AHC.
O salutaris hostia	AHC.
ELVEY, STEPHEN (1805–1860)	
Evening Service in A	N.
GARRETT, GEORGE M. (1834–1897)	
Evening Service in D	N.
Prepare ye the way of the Lord	N.
GOSS, JOHN (1800–1880)	
Evening Service in E	N.
Almighty and merciful God	N.
Come, and let us return unto the Lord	N.
God so loved the world	N.
I heard a voice from heaven	N.
If we believe that Jesus died	N.
Lift up thine eyes round about	N.
Lord, let me know mine end	N.
O Saviour of the world	N.
O taste, and see	N.
Praise the Lord, O my soul	N.
The wilderness	N.
NOBLE, T. TERTIUS (1867–1953)	
Morning and Evening Service in A	BA.
Morning and Evening Service in A minor	BA.
Magnificat and **Nunc dimittis** in B minor	BA.
OUSELEY, FREDERICK A. GORE (1825–1889)	
From the rising of the sun	N.
How goodly are Thy tents	N.
Is it nothing to you?	N.
It came even to pass	N.
O Saviour of the world	N.
PARRY, C. HUBERT H. (1848–1918)	
Hear my words, ye people	N.
(See also Volume 5)	
SMART, HENRY (1813–1879)	
Te Deum and Communion Service in F	N.
Evening Service in B flat	N.
Evening Service in F	N.
Evening Service in G	N.

STAINER, JOHN (1840–1901)

God so loved the world (from 'The Crucifixion')	N.
How beautiful upon the mountains ('from Awake, awake; put on thy strength, O Zion')	N.
I saw the Lord	N.

STANFORD, CHARLES VILLIERS (1852–1924)

Morning, Communion and Evening Service in B flat (contains the **Te Deum**)	N.
Morning, Communion and Evening Service in F	N.
Evening Service in A	N.
And I saw another angel	N.
If thou shalt confess with thy mouth	N.
The Lord is my shepherd	N.
(See also Volume 5)	

STEGGALL, CHARLES (1826–1905)

Remember now thy Creator	N.

SULLIVAN, ARTHUR S. (1842–1900)

Yea, though I walk (from 'The Light of the World')	CR.

WALMISLEY, THOMAS ATTWOOD (1814–1856)

Evening Service in B flat	N.
Evening Service in D	N.
Magnificat and Nunc dimittis in D minor	N.
From all that dwell below the skies	BO.
Hear, O Thou shepherd of Israel	N.
If the Lord Himself had not been on our side	N.
Ponder my words (for 4 sopranos)	RSCM.
Remember, O Lord, what is come upon us	N.

WESLEY, SAMUEL (1766–1837)

Sing aloud with gladness (Exultate Deo)	N.
When Israel came out of Egypt (In exitu Israel)	N.

WESLEY, SAMUEL SEBASTIAN (1810–1876)

Cathedral Service in F	N.
Evening Service in E	N.
All go unto one place	N.
Ascribe unto the Lord	BA. N.
Blessed be the God and Father	N.
Cast me not away from Thy presence	N.

Let us lift up our heart	AHC.
Man that is born of a woman	N.
O give thanks unto the Lord	AHC.
O Lord, my God	N.
O Lord, Thou art my God	N.
Praise the Lord, my soul	AHC.
The face of the Lord	OUP.
The Lord is my shepherd	N.
The wilderness	N.
Thou wilt keep him in perfect peace	BA.
Wash me thoroughly from my wickedness	N.

KEY

AHC.	Ascherberg, Hopwood and Crew (incorporating Bayley & Ferguson and Cary)
BA.	Banks
BO.	Bosworth
CMS.	Church Music Society
N.	Novello
CR.	Cramer
OUP.	Oxford University Press
RSCM.	Royal School of Church Music

Such items as are out of print may be consulted in the Colles Library of the Royal School of Church Music, Addington Palace, Addington, Surrey, England.

Charles Villiers Stanford by Orpen, from Trinity College, Cambridge
(by kind permission of the Master and Fellows)

BIBLIOGRAPHY

Bumpus, John S.: *A history of English Cathedral Music.* 2 vols. (T. Werner Laurie, 1908.)

Clutton, Cecil and Niland, Austin: *The British Organ.* (Batsford, 1963.)

Davies, H. Walford and Grace, Harvey: *Music and Worship.* (Eyre and Spottiswoode, 1935.)

Douglas, Winfred: *Church Music in History and Practice.* (Scribner, 1964.)

Fellowes, E. H.: *English Cathedral Music.* (Methuen, 1941.); *Organists and Masters of the Choristers of St. George's Chapel in Windsor.* (S.P.C.K., 1939.)

Fuller-Maitland, J. A.: *English Music in the XIXth century.* (Grant Richards, 1902.)

Grove's Dictionary of Music and Musicians. Fifth edition. (Macmillan, 1954. Supplementary Volume, 1961.)

Hadow, W. H.: *English Music.* (Longmans, Green & Co., 1931.)

Jacobs, Arthur (ed.): *Choral Music.* (Penguin Books, 1963.)

Jebb, John: *The Choral Responses and Litanies of the United Church of England and Ireland.* (George Bell, 1847.); *The Choral Service of the United Church of England and Ireland.* (John W. Parker, 1843.)

Mason, William: *Essays, Historical and Critical, on English Church Music.* (York; W. Blanchard, 1795.)

Nicholson, Sydney H.: *Quires and Places Where They Sing.* (S.P.C.K., 1932.)

Ouseley, F. A. Gore (ed.): *Special Anthems for Certain Seasons.* (Robert Cocks, 1861.)

Phillips, C. Henry: *The Singing Church.* (Faber and Faber, 1945.)

Phillips, C. S.: *Hymnody Past and Present.* (S.P.C.K., 1937.)

Routley, Erik: *The Church and Music.* (Duckworth, 1950.); *The Music of Christian Hymnody.* (Independent Press, 1957.)

Scholes, Percy: *The Mirror of Music.* (Novello and Oxford University Press, 1947.); *The Oxford Companion to Music.* Ninth edition. (Oxford University Press, 1955.)

Shaw, H. Watkins: *The Three Choirs Festival.* (Ebenezer Baylis, 1954.)

Stewart, C. Wauchope: *Music in Church Worship.* (Henderson, 1926.)

Walker, Ernest: *A History of Music in England.* Third edition, revised by Jack Westrup. (Oxford University Press, 1952.)

Wesley, S. S.: *A Few Words on Cathedral Music.* (Hinrichsen, 1961.)

West, John E.: *Cathedral Organists Past and Present.* (Novello, 1899.)

DISCOGRAPHY

GOSS, JOHN (1800–1880)	*If we believe that Jesus died*	St. John's College Choir, Cambridge (G. Guest)	RG406 **ZRG5406**
OUSELEY, FREDERICK GORE (1825–1889)	*From the rising of the sun*	St. Michael's College Choir Tenbury (L. Nethsingha)	RG423 **ZRG5423**
STAINER, JOHN (1840–1901)	*The Crucifixion*	Richard Lewis—tenor, Owen Brannigan—bass, St. John's College Choir, Cambridge, Brian Runnett—organ, (G. Guest)	RG320 **ZRG5320**
		Alexander Young—tenor, Donald Bell—baritone, Leeds Philharmonic Choir, Eric Chadwick—organ (H. Bardgett)	ALP1885 **ASD454**
	I saw the Lord	St. John's College Choir, Cambridge (G. Guest)	RG152 **ZRG5152**
STANFORD, CHARLES VILLIERS (1852–1924)	*The Lord is my shepherd, op. 38*	Magdalen College Choir, Oxford	AVM010
		See also Volume 5	
WALMISLEY, THOMAS ATTWOOD (1814–1856)	*Evening Service in D minor (Magnificat and Nunc Dimittis)*	St. John's College Choir, Cambridge (G. Guest)	RG406 **ZRG5406**
WESLEY, SAMUEL SEBASTIAN (1810–1876)	*The Wilderness*	St. John's College Choir, Cambridge (G. Guest)	
	Thou wilt keep him in perfect peace		
	Blessed be the God and Father		RG406 **ZRG5406**

KEY

ALP **ASD**	H.M.V.
AVM	ALPHA
RG **ZRG**	ARGO

* A recording of music from this volume, by the choir of St. Paul's Cathedral, has been made by H.M.V.